"You're chasing an illusion!"

André's voice was hard. "I don't give your marriage a chance." He paused deliberately. "You won't remain faithful more than a month."

"How dare you!" Beside herself with fury, Siane lifted a hand to strike his cheek. But his arms went around her, holding her closer than ever before. His lips found hers and the blood in her veins seemed to ignite with a fierce joy.

Then with a strength she didn't know she possessed, she broke away from him and ran. It was bad enough that he should think her wanton—for him to know the truth would be totally unacceptable. The truth! *I'm in love with him!* The words blazed through her mind like a burning streak of lightning.

Other titles by

ROSEMARY CARTER
IN HARLEQUIN PRESENTS

Other titles by

ROSEMARY CARTER
IN HARLEQUIN ROMANCES

Peggy M

ROSEMARY CARTER

my darling spitfire

Harlequin Books

TORONTO·LONDON·NEW YORK·AMSTERDAM
SYDNEY·HAMBURG·PARIS·STOCKHOLM

Harlequin Presents edition published February 1980
ISBN 0-373-10337-9

Original hardcover edition published in 1979
by Mills & Boon Limited

CHAPTER ONE

WILGESPRUIT! Just a tiny railway siding. Siane had noted already that the train stopped at such places barely long enough to blink an eye and register a name on a weathered board. Quickly she gathered her belongings and hurried from the compartment to the exit.

In her haste she did not register the man who was proceeding to the same point at a more leisurely pace. Somehow she managed to get her suitcase past him to the door. But when she tried to lift the plastic bag down the steps, the man's body seemed to deflect its passage, so that the precious bag was wrenched from her arms and slithered a little way along the concrete platform.

With a gasp of indignation Siane shouldered past the man, managing to alight before he did. By the time she turned on him, hugging her bag, and the blue eyes of her Irish grandmother spitting fire in a flushed oval face, the train was gathering speed on the tracks.

She had drawn herself up to her full height, but even then she had to tilt her head back to see his face. 'I think an apology is called for!' she threw at him accusingly.

'Outraged femininity in the middle of the bushveld.' A mocking glance came from a face that was rugged and deeply bronzed. 'Odd, I'd have thought the apology should come from you.'

'From me?' Icy tones, befitting her indignation. 'My bag might have been ruined!'

'Entirely through your own impatience.' There was no hint of apology in his tone. Grey eyes flicked her insolently for a moment, noting the anger that heightened the colour in her cheeks, then descending slowly to take in the curves of a slender but intensely feminine figure. When he met her eyes again he looked amused. 'I don't imagine patience is one of your virtues, so I won't remind you that you did the pushing and that you should be the one to apologise.' Giving her no time to reply, he added, 'Need any help?'

Under normal circumstances, Siane would have responded warmly to the unexpected question, but the arrogance in the man's tone made that impossible. 'No, thanks,' she said stiffly.

Without a word he left her, walking away with a stride that was long and easy and unhampered by the heavy-looking cases he held in each hand.

With a slight effort she wrenched her eyes away from his receding back as she considered her next step. For a moment she wondered if she had been foolish to refuse the offer of help. But no.... She had known when she left Johannesburg that on her arrival at Wilgespruit she would have to find a way of continuing her journey, and tall arrogant men had hardly figured in her plans.

'What will you do when you get there?' her father had questioned dubiously, and her mother had voiced her despair with, 'I wish I knew where you came by your impulsiveness!'

To all of which Siane had answered quietly and reassuringly, but with a firmness which had allowed no thwarting of her intentions. It was not possible to plan the whole journey from Johannesburg. According to the map, Wilgespruit was the nearest point on the main line to Crocodile View, the private game park where John worked. When she reached the station she would enquire about taxis or a connecting train.

The first part of the train journey had been uneventful, and she had no reason to think that the next part would not be equally so. It was just a question of finding out what she must do.

She put down her things and looked about her. If a stationmaster existed at Wilgespruit, he had evidently taken his leave before the dust had had time to settle once more between the tracks. A peep into a small shack, obviously an office of sorts, revealed no sign of life. With the departure of the tall arrogant man the platform was deserted. For the first time Siane felt the slightest flicker of doubt. For a moment she caught herself wishing that she had not dismissed the offer of help out of hand.

Which was nonsense, she told herself firmly as she walked along the platform and surveyed the countryside. As the wife of a game-ranger she would have to learn to be resourceful. There would be times of loneliness. Not real loneliness, of course, for there would always be John's company to look forward to at the end of the day. Yet there would be occasions when she would have to make decisions on her own, and when she might have to cope with emergencies. The sooner she started the learning process the better it would be—on more than one count, for the sky was a leaden grey, and a storm-presaging hush had settled over the veld.

It was not easy to manage her belongings, but somehow she managed. The plastic bag and the carton of cookies were hoisted in place between her arm and her body; the other hand held the suitcase. At the edge of the station platform she saw what the shack had previously concealed from view. There was a sprawl of scattered houses about a quarter of a mile away. Thin spirals of smoke rose from chimneys. She was not alone.

A small pointed chin tilted bravely upwards as Siane fixed her eyes on the distant houses. Perhaps her mother was right when she called her impulsive. At this moment it would seem like heaven if John were to materialise beside her with a car, if he would kiss her and load up her luggage, and drive her back with him to the game park. But John did not know that she was coming. It had seemed such a wonderful idea to surprise him.

And it *would* be wonderful. The present uncertainty was only temporary, all part of the adventure she had always longed for. The ominous sky above the silent veld, the continuation of her journey through the bush, these were facets of the adventure. There would be John's astonishment when he saw her, his further astonishment when she opened the bag and showed him the wedding-dress. The dress! The storm could begin at any time and it must not get wet. Urgency lent strength to tired arms.

The inn was in the centre of the hamlet. The office was empty, but when she pressed a bell for service a blank-faced clerk appeared. He scratched his head when Siane asked for directions to Crocodile View Game Park. There was no connecting train, he said. Taxis? There were none at Wilgespruit. A bus? Yes, there was a bus twice a week. The next bus would leave on Friday.

Friday! Today was Wednesday. 'I *must* get to Crocodile View,' Siane said, a little despairingly.

'Have to wait till Friday,' came the laconic answer.

'Two days....' Blue eyes were clouded. What should she do? Was the sensible thing to phone John? Even if her arrival at Crocodile View was not quite as she had planned it, there would still be the element of surprise.

She did not know the phone number of the game park, but the desk clerk would have it. 'I'd like to phone Crocodile View,' she said.

'Sorry, miss.' A shake of the head.

'They must have a phone,' she said disbelievingly.

'The line is broken. Bad storm a few days ago.'

'Oh dear!' A frown creased the smooth forehead. 'Well, then ... do you have a room for me?'

Something in her expression must have reached him, for he helped her carry her possessions up the stairs. The room was small and sparsely furnished— just a bed with a faded tweed bedspread, a night table and a mirror—but it was clean.

When the door had closed behind the clerk, Siane sat down on the bed. Two days to wait. What would she do with herself? In her suitcase was a paper-back novel, but it would not take her long to read. How would she pass the time after that?

She remembered her resolve to be resourceful. Here was her first test. She stood up and went to the window. Outside, the scene was one of desolation. The sky had grown even darker, a heavy greyness streaked by sporadic flashes of lightning. It was not raining yet, but a wind had risen. In the fields the mielies were bending beneath it, and the gum trees creaked.

Wilgespruit.... In English the name meant a stream with willows. Tomorrow perhaps the weather would clear, and then she would go for a long walk. She would find the stream, have a picnic beneath the willows.

But there was still today to get through, the after-noon and the evening. The thought of spending the hours until dinner alone in the tiny room was un-appealing. Leading off from the office she had seen what looked like a lounge. She would sit there a while, order a cold drink perhaps. Thank heavens she had brought enough money to see her through the next few days.

The walk from the station had left her dusty and dishevelled. After a shower and a change of clothing she felt better. Before she left the room she made up her face. Nobody would see her, except perhaps the desk clerk whom she had no desire to impress, but Siane had not reached the age of twenty-three without learning that a woman often feels as good as she looks. A smidgin of blue shadow and a touch of mascara made a difference. Siane glanced at herself in the mirror. Blue eyes stared back at her from a small oval face in a frame of glossy dark curls. Her spirits lifted. If the make-up was bravado, it was also a morale-booster.

The lounge was empty. Like Siane's room, it was clean enough but the furniture was shabby and the decor uninspiring. She hesitated at the door, uncertain whether to go in, but the only alternative was the claustrophobic smallness of her room. If a choice had to be made this was the better place to spend her time. There was a pile of magazines on a table. She could look through them, very slowly, and perhaps by the time she had come to the bottom of the pile the wind would have died or it would be time for dinner.

She sat down on a two-seater settee, and, finding an article on poaching, she began to read. Anything that had to do with animals in their natural environment was part of John's work, and as such was of interest to Siane as well. So it had been for as long as she could remember. John had always loved animals, and because throughout the years he had been her cherished companion she had made it her business to learn whatever she could about animals so that he would enjoy being with her.

She was deep in the article when someone said, 'Mind if I join you?'

She looked up, startled. But as she took in the face of the man gazing down at her, she relaxed. He was young and good-looking with a dimple in one cheek and green eyes that twinkled.

'Please do,' she smiled, and then, more uncertainly, as he sat down beside her on the settee instead of on a chair as she had expected, 'I was beginning to wonder if I was the only guest in the place.'

'What a waste that would be!' His smile was so approving that she could not take offence at his meaning. 'Place starts filling up around now. It's a travellers' inn.' He saw her puzzled expression. 'Travelling salesmen. We spend the night at Wilgespruit before moving on to the next place. What will you drink?'

'A Coke would be nice.'

'That's a very soft drink for a big girl,' he teased her. 'Have something stronger. Brandy?'

'Coke,' she said firmly.

'Strong-minded female!' An eyebrow lifted, but his lips curved in a smile which was so boyish that it robbed the words of any sting. 'But pretty. Very pretty.' He leaned towards her. 'Be a devil and change your mind about a brandy.'

'You said I was strong-minded,' she reminded him

with a smile, which hid the beginnings of nervousness.

'But so am I. Soften up, pretty girl—the day is young, as the saying goes. You and I can have fun.'

'Thanks, but I'll just stick to Coke.' She tried, as tactfully as she was able, to manoeuvre herself further to her side of the settee. The drinks were brought and she watched him down a brandy in a single gulp. 'What do you sell, Mr ... I don't think I know your name.'

'Kruger. Marnie Kruger. And your name is Siane O'Brien. I saw it in the register.'

'What do you sell, Mr Kruger?' she was becoming more uncomfortable by the minute.

'Ladies' underwear.' An arm slid behind her back to grip her shoulder. 'How about a modelling session, Siane?'

Siane's nature was impulsive. She was also gentle, and possessed an innate dislike of hurting people. But beneath the gentleness, and dramatic when provoked, lurked a temper which, together with her blue eyes, was the legacy of her Irish grandmother. That temper was now surging to the fore. 'Leave me alone, Mr Kruger!' she hissed.

'Come, my pretty,' the smile had lost its boyishness and was now frankly lascivious, 'I thought we were going to have fun together.'

'You've picked the wrong girl, Mr Kruger.' Siane tried to struggle away from him, but the hand on her shoulder had tightened, the fingers biting painfully into her flesh.

She opened her mouth to scream for help, but he forestalled her. A hand clamped over her mouth. In the handsome face was a lust which even her untutored eyes could distinguish.

Fear was mixed now with her anger. Even if she managed to scream it was dubious whether anybody would come to her help. Travellers' inn this might be, but so far it seemed Mr Kruger was the only salesman to book in. As far as the clerk was concerned, she doubted whether he would come to her help and so risk offending a customer who was probably lucrative.

One more lesson in resourcefulness, she thought, as she sank her teeth into the hand that covered her mouth.

There was a yelp of pain. As Mr Kruger's injured hand shot back from her mouth, Siane took her moment. In an instant she had jumped from the settee and was making for the door. But he was quicker than she was. He caught at her from behind, and turned her roughly to him again. There was venom in his expression as he lifted the other hand to strike her.

In the instant before the hand could find its target the man was yanked upwards. A few foul epithets spat out from contorted lips, only to fade abruptly as Marnie Kruger stared into the granite face of the man who towered above him. Siane's eyes widened in disbelief. The man who held her would-be molester by the collar of his jacket was none other than the man with whom she had had the brush at the station.

'What the hell do you think you're doing?' Marnie Kruger rasped angrily.

'Breaking up an ugly scene.' The tall man's lips were tight, but the look he threw Siane was mocking.

A hand was held up for inspection, teeth marks still fresh on the palm. 'She bit me, the little bitch!'

'Careful!' Easily Siane's rescuer shook Mr Kruger, then threw him from him. 'I've no doubt the assault was provoked.'

If Mr Kruger had an answer—and he would not hesitate to make up a lie, Siane knew—the bigger man's strength must have intimidated him. He opened his mouth, closed it again, glowered at Siane, then slunk from the room.

'Thank you,' Siane began shakily. 'You rescued me from....'

'A fate worse than death?' Grey eyes gleamed. 'Not quite that in this day and age, I think. But a nasty situation, granted.'

She bit back a retort. For the moment this man was her only ally at the inn. Quietly she said, 'He offered me something to drink. I had no idea he had anything else in mind.'

'You've only yourself to blame.'

He had spoken so conversationally that for a moment she stared at him, wondering if she had heard him correctly. He was watching her, a slight smile sketching the corners of sensuous lips. She remembered his insolent manner at the station, and anger surged through her.

'You make me sound like a tart!'

He laughed mockingly. 'Most tarts are more sophisticated than you. No, Miss O'Brien, what I meant was that for an attractive female travelling alone you place yourself in peculiarly vulnerable situations. How old are you? All of eighteen?'

'Twenty-three,' she said with dignity.

'That old?' Again the glint of laughter. 'I'd have thought that a female of your advanced age would know better than to get all dressed up and sit in the lounge of a travelling man's hotel unless she was open to advances.'

Quite cheerfully she could have slapped his face. But there had been enough violence for one day. 'It won't happen again,' she said quietly. 'I'm going straight to my room.'

'Not without your supper. The gong will be sounding any time now. Come, Miss O'Brien, you'll eat with me.'

In a sense she was relieved. The presence of the authoritative and powerfully-built man at her table would ensure that she would not be pestered again. But there was something about the arrogant tone of the invitation—he seemed to have taken her agreement for granted—which prompted at least a token resistance.

'I'm not certain I want to,' she said stiffly.

'You'd rather have the attentions of your obnoxious friend once more?' Grey eyes mocked her.

'Why should you care what happens to me?' Blue eyes flashed defiantly. 'You said I was to blame for what happened.'

'I don't care in the least.' His voice was cool. 'But the owner of this hotel is a friend of mine, and I do care about him. He's in hospital at the moment, and he wouldn't be happy if an ugly incident caused bad publicity.' A strong hand gripped her arm. 'Come along, Miss O'Brien.'

Anger deepened inside her. For sheer arrogance she had never met the equal of the man. But she had to still the anger, at least for the moment, for there was something in what he said. The encounter in the lounge had left her shaken, and she was not in the mood for any more unpleasantness. With this man at her side it was unlikely that anything further would happen.

She was intensely aware of him as she walked with him to the dining-room. If he was the most arrogant person she had ever met, he was also the most arresting in a physical sense. He was tall, even taller than she had first realised. Even through his jacket she saw that his shoulders were broad, and so was the chest which tapered to a narrow waist. The cut of well-tailored trousers revealed legs that were long and taut. A little shiver passed through her, which she instantly suppressed. Just because she had never met anyone quite so compellingly and aggressively masculine, it did not mean that she should let herself be intimidated. After tonight she would never see him again anyway. She lifted her chin mutinously, as if to convince herself of a point.

The action was not lost on him. There was a low chuckle close beside her, too close.... It was the most sensuous sound she had heard, and she felt the tremor which ran through her nerve-stream.

'I amuse you?' she asked, low-toned.

'A little. Are you preparing to ward off another attack?'

'Am I in for one?' She felt foolish the moment she had asked the question.

'Not from me,' he said politely, but she saw the mockery in his eyes. 'I don't molest children.'

'I am *not* a child!' Rebelliously she threw the words at him.

'No?' Another chuckle. 'You'll convince me of that when you begin to behave like an adult. This is our table. Sit down.'

The last words were said quietly, but nevertheless they had the ring of command. For a moment Siane hesitated, moved with the wish to defy him. But defiance would make her seem even more childish in his eyes, and would only increase his contempt. Without a word she sat down.

She took her time about studying the short menu. When she looked up he was watching her. 'Ready to order?' he asked, and amusement was once more in his eyes, for the menu was short and the selection so limited that only a few moments were required to read it. He knew she had been playing for time.

'Of course. I'll start with the soup.' She forced herself to meet his gaze. 'By the way, how did you know my name? From the register?'

'Of course. Siane O'Brien, and you come from Johannesburg. Single, I presume, or have you left your wedding ring at home?'

'Engaged to a man who does not happen to consider me a child,' she said tartly. 'I haven't looked at the register myself. . . .'

'Connors. André Connors,' he informed her. And then, when they had given the waiter their order: 'Your fiancé doesn't object to your travelling in the bushveld without him?'

So he was still out to make her feel like a child. Well, she would show him. 'Not at all.' She threw him her most dazzling smile. 'As it happens, I'm on my way to marry him.'

'Congratulations.' He was unperturbed by her charm. 'The soup is getting cold. Eat up. You really will be needing the sustenance.'

His tone was polite, making his meaning all the more outrageous. She threw him a flaming look, but the eyes that met hers were cool and amused. What would be John's reaction if he were here? Would he hit this man very hard, as he deserved? Or would he smile and shrug the insolence off as a joke? At the thought of her fiancé her nerves steadied. John would not fight. He was strong, but gentle with it. He did not see the sense in fighting —and he was right. There was no dignity left when one lowered oneself to the level of animals. Too often Siane's temper got the better of her. John would be good for her. She had been too long without his steady good sense.

She dropped her eyes to her plate. For a while there was silence. Things were not turning out quite as she had planned, Siane thought, as she began to eat. By now she should have been at the game park, and she and John should have been busy with plans for the wedding. Instead, she was eating dinner in the company of a stranger whose rugged masculinity was making her react in a manner quite alien to her.

She lifted her head to find him watching her. In the grey eyes was a quality which was hard to define but which made her feel even more unsettled than before. She wondered what he did for a living. His rugged features gave him a look of uncompromising toughness, the look of a man who was not frightened of danger. He was not handsome in a conventional way, she decided, and yet his appearance was not one she would easily forget. It was a combination of toughness and sensuousness, coupled with a suggestion of latent savageness. For no reason she shivered.

She was letting his personality affect her in the most ridiculous way. She had lifted her head with the purpose of asking a question, and ask it she would.

'Mr Connors, do you know a private game park called Crocodile View?'

His voice was even. 'I know it very well.'

'You do?' she breathed. And then, as a new thought struck her, 'Do you work there?'

'Nearby.'

She did not know that her eyes became luminous;

or that her lips parted slightly to reveal small perfectly-shaped teeth. 'Are you on your way there?'

A curt nod of the head.

'Tonight?' She stopped breathing as she waited for his answer.

'Tomorrow.'

'That's marvellous!' she exclaimed, forgetting her fear of him. 'Then I don't need to wait for the bus. I can go with you and. . . .'

'You are not going anywhere with me.' His voice was hard as he interrupted her.

'But ... but you said you're going that way, and. . . .' She paused, and the light left her eyes as she gazed at him in confusion. More quietly now she asked, 'you don't want to give me a lift?'

'My turn to ask the questions.' The implacability in his expression was ominous. 'Firstly, why are you going to Crocodile View?'

She lifted her chin. 'My reason shouldn't matter to you.'

'You're asking the favour, lady.'

There was no verbal way in which she could get the better of him. A sardonic grin lifted the corners of a mobile mouth. He knew that the taunt had angered her. However, if she wanted him to take her with him she would have to answer his question.

'I'm on my way to join my fiancé,' she told him.

'His name?'

'John Lang.'

Something came and went in the grey eyes, so quickly that she wondered if she had imagined it.

'Interesting,' he said enigmatically.

She looked at him for a moment without speaking, wondering why just one word, said with a particular inflection, should have the power to make her feel quite so young and vulnerable and uncertain. At length she asked uncertainly, 'Do you know John?'

'Of course.'

'He ... he must have mentioned me.'

'Not that I recall.'

Once more there was something in the way he spoke that made her feel uneasy. She made a mental note that André Connors would not be a favourite guest when she and John entertained. Small white teeth went out to catch a soft lower lip. Then she said firmly, 'I'm not surprised. Johnny doesn't talk about his private affairs to every stranger.'

'He's a wise man,' was the laconic comment.

They could spend hours sparring, Siane realised. Better to come to the point and settle the issue one way or the other.

She repeated the question in as confident a tone as she could muster, so that he would have no option but to agree. 'Will you give me a lift?'

'You know the answer already.'

'John would want you to.' She could not remember being spoken to with such curtness. 'I ... I know he would.'

'Does John know you're coming?'

'No. ...'

'I thought not. Despite what you say about his

reticence'—another brief grin—'I think he would have mentioned the arrival of something so momentous as a wife-to-be.'

'I wanted to surprise him.' Siane bit her lip. 'When I found out about the bus I thought I'd phone Crocodile View, but the line is out of order.'

'I see.' He looked at her thoughtfully, the eyes narrowed and inscrutable.

She looked at him hopefully. 'There's really no point in discussing it?'

'None at all. Except to suggest that you catch the next train back to Johannesburg.'

Siane looked at him for a long moment, trying unsuccessfully to probe the thoughts behind the rugged mask of his face. When she spoke again the defiance was back in her tone. 'I don't know what you're getting at, Mr Connors, but if you're trying to put me off you certainly haven't succeeded. I don't give up easily. If I can't find another way of getting to Crocodile View I'll catch the bus on Friday.'

A touch of amusement glimmered briefly in the eyes which studied her across the table. She held her breath, angry at the insolence of his scrutiny, and bracing herself for what she instinctively felt would be a sarcastic comment. But there was just an unconcerned lifting of one eyebrow. 'As you wish,' he said coolly.

So he *was* trying to put her off! She shot him an icy glare before turning with determination to the meal which now tasted like cardboard.

For a while they ate in silence. Siane was in no mood for small-talk, and the silence did not seem to bother her arrogant companion. She noticed that he ate with enjoyment. If the interchange had infuriated her, it had not given him a moment's frustration.

Now and then, when his eyes were on his plate, she was able to study him unobserved. He was altogether the most insufferable man she had ever met, she decided crossly. His clothes were probably quite ordinary. On any other man they would pass unnoticed, yet on André Connors they seemed to denote good tailoring and a certain amount of expense. The hands that held the fork and knife were long and tanned, the fingers well shaped. Strong hands, Siane thought, and capable. She had already experienced those fingers in a grip on her arm, and now, quite involuntarily, she wondered how they would feel in a caress. Heavens, was she quite mad? She had decided that André Connors was everything she most disliked in a man, yet here she was, wondering how it would feel to be caressed by him. Determinedly she dropped her eyes to her food and forced herself to eat. Yet the compulsion to look up again some moments later was irresistible. If the man repulsed her, he fascinated her at the same time.

His head lifted quite suddenly, catching her off guard. As grey eyes met blue ones there was the familiar mocking gleam. Impossible as it seemed that he should know she had been studying him,

Siane had the unsettling idea that he did know. It was an idea which came from the instinctive conviction that André Connors would be aware of most things which took place within his orbit.

'I was just wondering,' she remarked, as calmly as she was able, 'why you're so set against taking me with you.'

A slight shrug. 'I thought we'd settled the subject.'

It came to her all at once. 'You think the trip might be too rough for me, don't you?' She wondered why she had not thought of this before. As she saw his eyebrows rise speculatively she felt she was right. 'I'm not the princess sleeping on the pea, Mr Connors.'

'Really?' Strong white teeth flashed in a wicked grin. 'Are you inviting me to test the softness of your mattress, so that I can prove the point for myself?'

She caught her breath at the sheer insolence of the remark. 'How dare you, Mr Connors! Wait till I tell John!'

'You imagine he'll react like a prim virgin? Grow up, little Miss O'Brien.'

Little Miss O'Brien! He made her sound like a schoolgirl, innocent and naïve. Temper flared inside her, quick and hot, and she longed to fly at him with every epithet at her command. With a supreme effort of will she managed to hold herself back, feeling that it might be in her best interests if she did not make a second enemy in one day. The time would come, and soon, she hoped, when she would be able to tell Mr André Connors precisely what she thought of him!

Nevertheless, she knew that she had never been put in her place quite so ruthlessly, nor so outrageously. Colour came and went in her cheeks, and her breathing quickened as she stared at him. He looked back at her steadily, unabashed. She knew in a moment that she could not sustain the gaze, but would be the first to drop her eyes. With a jerky movement she put down her knife and fork, and without another word she moved abruptly from the table. André Connors watched her, unrepentant. He made no effort to apologise or detain her.

CHAPTER TWO

THE room seemed even smaller than before, she thought, as she stood at the window and stared moodily outside. The storm had still not broken, but the gloom was oppressive. It was a gloom which hung not only over the unnaturally silent veld, but which filtered in through the window, making the proximity of the four walls unbearably claustrophobic.

Quickly Siane slipped a cardigan over her shoulders and ran down the steps. André Connors was nowhere to be seen, and she was glad. Her nerves were still so raw from his abrasive manner that she was in no mood for another encounter.

It was not much easier to breathe out of doors than it had been in the narrow confines of the room. The air was sultry and heavy. Earlier there had been a wind, but that had now dropped. The blue-gums stood straight once more, dry and dusty and tense with waiting, and in the fields the mielie plants did not stir. Not a dog barked, not a bird sang. It was as if the bushveld lay girded and waiting for the inevitable storm.

She would stay within reach of the inn, Siane decided. She would walk just far enough to get the feel of the place. A narrow path skirted a mielie-field, and seeing a clump of willows in the distance she decided to stroll a little way along it. She had not gone far when the first drops fell and she had to turn back.

The path had taken a twist. One way led to the distant willows, the other to the back of the inn. A few vehicles stood in the yard, a truck, a station-wagon, several dust-coated cars. One of the vehicles would belong to the amorous Mr Kruger, Siane thought with a grimace. She had forgotten him in the last half hour. André Connors really had rescued her from a situation with which she might not have been able to cope. For that she should have been grateful, but his arrogance had not lent itself to any graciousness on her part.

A new thought struck her. Did André Connors think she had deliberately encouraged the other man's attentions? Was that the reason he did not want her at Crocodile View? Possibly he saw her as some sort of wanton female, and felt that John needed protection. The idea was so absurd that she laughed out loud. Immediately she felt better.

Two days would pass. On Friday she would catch the bus to Crocodile View, and when John had recovered from his surprise he would laugh with her at what had happened.

She was just a few steps from the inn when a movement caught her attention, and she turned and saw a man at the truck. He was bending to take something from the front seat, then he straightened, and as he closed the door she saw he was André

Connors. He went back to the inn without glancing her way. So the truck was his. He must have parked it in the yard to await his return on the train. Such a big vehicle, she thought resentfully, yet he begrudged her a few inches of space.

The hours dragged. The paperback in her case had been chosen too quickly, and Siane found that it did not appeal to her after all. Or perhaps it was just that she was too restless to read.

She wondered now if she had been foolish to leave home with no definite plans. Wilgespruit had been a reassuring spot on a map, and there had been no doubt in her mind that the second part of the journey would be as simple as the first. Kissing her parents goodbye, she had laughed away their doubts, but for the first time now she ruefully conceded that they might have been right. Perhaps she really had been too impulsive. Rather than surprise John with her unexpected arrival, it might have been better to tell him she was coming. He would have given her directions and she would have managed the trip without difficulty.

She put aside the book. She was finding it hard to concentrate on the printed words. Outside the wind had risen once more, and the drizzle was rapidly turning into a tropical downpour. The rain lashed down on the tin roof of the inn, and the window was so hazy that it was impossible to see outside.

It seemed there was nothing to do but go to bed. As she undressed, slipping on a new nightgown made of silk and edged with lace, Siane's thoughts went quite involuntarily to André Connors. What was he doing? Could he be in the bar, laughing with Marnie Kruger at her expense? Somehow, although his manner had made her so angry that she was prepared to think the worst of him, it was a picture which did not fit. Perhaps he was reading, or writing a letter. He could even be asleep. *Could* he sleep through the storm?

She had a vivid picture of the man lying beneath a sheet. He would be bare from the waist up, and there would be dark hair clinging to a chest as bronzed as his arms and throat. Realising the drift her thoughts were taking, she gave an impatient exclamation and tried to push André Connors from her thoughts. He had no place there, just as she had no right to be thinking about him.

She was on her way to Crocodile View to be with John. In a few days they would be married. It did not occur to her to wonder where she would sleep until their wedding, or whether there was a church nearby. John would arrange things, just as he had done ever since she had known him.

As she lay in the dark and listened to the raging of the storm, her mind went back over the years to her childhood. From the time she had been a little girl John had been a part of her life. He had taken the place of the brother she had never had. He had also been her closest friend. Not her only friend. There had been girls at school with whom she had laughed and giggled and talked girl-talk. Over the years she had had a few 'best' friends, but after matriculating their path had veered in different directions, until all that remained were Christmas cards and occasional telephone calls. Today their names and faces were an indistinguishable blur.

John's friendship had been constant. It had begun when his parents had bought the house next door. His mother had worked all day and the lonely little boy had taken to spending much of his time in Siane's home, drawn to the warmth and love which he found there. Though John was a few years older than Siane—he would be twenty-seven now—almost from the very beginning an affinity had existed between them, one which did not dwindle with the passing of the years. Even when John was no longer dependent on the security of Siane's home, his affection for his little playmate had remained. He had protected her from aggression at school, and had included her in many of his social activities. His friends would sometimes tease him about the little girl who followed him wherever he went, but John laughed them off with such good humour that the boys grew used to having Siane around.

But the best times were the ones when they were alone together. Those days were spent mostly out of doors, especially the week-ends. The suburb where they lived was on the outskirts of town, and not far away were vast tracts of undeveloped land. In the long wind-blown grass were the tiny animals of the veld, and in the thorny branches of the acacias were the nests of the wild birds. Sometimes they would see a meerkat scampering through a clearing, or a lizard slithering across a sun-baked rock. There were snakes, and John taught Siane to distinguish the harmless grass-snakes from the deadly cobras and mambas. He would tell her about the birds and the animals, about their habits and the ways in which they built their homes.

Now and then they would visit a farm about twenty miles out of town, belonging to John's uncle. There John was in his element. And again he would be teaching, explaining, and Siane, always an avid listener, would try to follow all he said.

He confided in her his dreams for the future. At first he toyed with the idea of becoming a vet. It was only later that his thoughts turned to being a game warden. The only thing that never changed was his interest in animals. And always Siane moulded her thoughts to his, even to the extent of reading more about the things he told her so that she would be able to talk with him about the subject which so absorbed him.

On leaving school John had in fact become a vet, and for a while he had assisted in another man's practice. He had enjoyed the work, but while he attended to the illnesses of domestic animals, his greater ambition had never deserted him. He still dreamed of becoming a game warden. A year ago the opportunity he had been awaiting for so long finally presented itself when he was offered a position at Crocodile View.

Siane, who was engaged to him by this time, had assumed that she would be going with him, but

John had felt it wiser to wait a while. When he was settled at the game park and could be certain about the future, they would be married. He would take a week's leave, and the wedding would be in Johannesburg where both sets of parents still lived.

With this plan Siane had been content. While she missed John, she was sensible enough to know that the parting was temporary. Soon he would be settled and then they would be together always. The time passed fairly quickly, and there was little opportunity to mope. Her days were spent in the nursery school where she worked as a teacher, and evenings and week-ends were taken up with preparing a trousseau and stitching a wedding-dress.

And all the time there had been John's letters to look forward to. At first they came regularly, one a week, sometimes two, enthusiastic and eager, full of news and details. Siane would read them many times, and as she did so she would wonder how she would adapt to a life that was different from anything she had ever known. There was loneliness, John wrote, and wide open spaces where human beings took second place to the animals which roamed at will. There was joy in the letters, John's happiness at doing what he had always dreamed of radiating through his words.

In the last few months however the frequency of the letters had changed. Sometimes ten days would elapse before she heard from him, sometimes more. The diminished frequency was not what worried her the most. John never complained of his work or his living conditions, the letters themselves were as newsy as ever. But between the lines Siane, perceptive to his every mood, sensed despondency and a lack of his earlier enthusiasm. She wrote and asked if he was ill, but he denied it. She did not believe him. Perhaps he had been ill and did not want her to worry. Or perhaps something had happened to make him unhappy. Whatever the cause, she wanted to be with him, to share his life and his problems, to give him physical and spiritual support when he needed it. He had said that he would send for her when he was ready. She would no longer wait, she decided. John needed her now. When he saw her he would be glad that she had come.

Siane could not remember a particular day when John had proposed to her. Over the years it had gradually been taken for granted that they would be married. After her parents, Siane loved John more than anyone else in the world, and she knew that her feelings were reciprocated. She could no more imagine a life without him than she could imagine functioning without an arm. Theirs would be a loving relationship, happy and peaceful and infinitely comfortable. It might never be passionate in the way that books and movies depicted romance —they knew each other too well for that—but its essential quality of loving tranquillity would transcend the excitement of passion.

She frowned as she stared into the darkness. It was foreign to her nature to be so introspective. She had never associated passion with her feelings for

John, and she wondered why she did so now.

Restlessly she shifted her head on the pillow. Vaguely she understood that her thoughts were in some way connected with the arrogant André Connors, and the realisation gave her little comfort. If anything, her dislike for the man grew.

Perhaps it was just the unsettling events of the day which had thrown her mind into confusion. Nothing had gone quite as planned, and so much else had happened. There was the unexpected difficulty of reaching Crocodile View, the unfortunate encounter with the lustful salesman. Last of all there had been the interchange with André Connors. Surprisingly, it was this which had unsettled her more than anything else.

If she was to get any sleep, first she would have to calm a troubled mind. If only John was with her now! When he was around, there was no turmoil. But John was at Crocodile View, so his image would have to help her instead. She tried to create a picture of him in her mind. It came to her with dismay that this was not as easy as it should be. A year's parting had left its mark. But she *would* do it. Slowly the well-loved features began to take form; the eyes which were as blue as her own, lips which curved easily in a boyish smile, a broad jaw which gave the face an attractive openness. The features merged until they formed a whole picture, and there he was, her John whom she had loved for as long as she could remember.

It was reassuring to have him securely in her

mind, more difficult to keep him there. For another image was edging him out; the eyes grey and mocking, the teeth white and strong, the lips hard and sensuous at the same time. Despairingly Siane tried to keep the one image from pushing away the other. But she was tired, very tired, and the struggle became too much for her. In the moments before she fell asleep it was the lean bronzed face with the mocking eyes which held precedence in her mind.

The room was dim and cool when Siane awoke the next morning. Leaving her bed, she went to the window, and shivered as her bare toes curled on the stone floor and a draught chilled her shoulders. After last night's storm the patch of garden below her window looked a little forlorn. Some time during the night the rain had stopped, but the sky was grey, with a half-hearted sun trying unsuccessfully to pierce the clouds.

It was very early, and it made sense to stay in bed a while longer before going in to the dining-room for breakfast. But it was cold in the gossamer nightgown, and besides, she had never felt more awake.

After a shower in a bathroom at the end of the passage, she dressed quickly in jeans and a pale blue sweater. The foyer was empty and there was nobody at the desk as she slipped out of the hotel.

She walked a little way along the path she had taken the day before. It was heavy going. The ground was muddy and tangles of fallen veld-grass clung damply to her jeans. For a while Siane resisted the temptation to go back, but at length the desolation of the wet veld got the better of her. As she emerged from the trail into the yard at the back of the inn, she wondered how on earth she would get through the next two days.

The parking lot was almost empty. It seemed that many of the travelling salesmen had already left. Beneath a tree stood a truck she recognised—it was the one belonging to André Connors.

On impulse she went across to the vehicle and tried the doors. They were locked. Standing on tiptoe, she looked into the open body of the truck and saw a layer of canvas. The canvas was dry. In addition to his other qualities, André Connors was practical, Siane conceded wryly. It was clear that he had left nothing in the truck to get wet in the storm. Whatever was here now had been packed this morning.

The idea came to her quite suddenly, and her breathing quickened as she stared into the canvas-covered truck-bottom. Could she do it? Would she dare? It was tempting, so very tempting.... But if Mr Connors found her out he would be furious.

The thought of his anger took her a few steps away from the truck. She did not need to witness his fury to know that it would be terrible. Slowly she walked to a door at the side of the inn. One hand was on the door knob when she turned thoughtfully back.

It was as if the canvases had been put in the truck just for her. She could lie beneath them and the driver of the truck would be unaware of his passenger. When their destination had been reached, she would find a way of leaving the truck unseen. André had said that he worked near Crocodile View. Somehow she would find a way to complete the rest of the journey.

It was unlikely that he would discover her presence. But if he did, the worst that could happen would be a furious tongue-lashing, and she was strong-minded enough to survive that.

Her mind was made up in an instant. Swiftly she slipped into the inn and up to her room. The fact that the truck was packed was an indication that André Connors was on the point of leaving.

Fortunately there was nothing to pay. Yesterday's deposit had covered accommodation for a day. It took Siane just a few minutes to fetch her luggage from her room. Out once more through the side entrance, and a deliberately nonchalant walk across the parking lot. Now for the worst part. If she was seen climbing into the truck there would be questions. Mercifully the yard was deserted. Siane's heart thumped wildly as she hoisted her luggage over the side. Another look around to make sure nobody was about, and then quickly into the truck. Bending low so that the sides of the vehicle kept her concealed, she hid the three pieces of luggage beneath the canvas, making sure that the suitcase, the bulkiest item, was in a corner. Then she crept beneath the canvas herself, and lay still, hoping that her slender form would not be easily discernible.

She did not have long to wait. Minutes after she had closed the canvas, brisk footsteps sounded in the parking-lot. Siane stopped breathing as the footsteps approached the back of the truck. An object was thrown on the canvas, just missing her. Then the footsteps moved to the front of the truck, and there was the sound of the engine starting. The vehicle began to move.

The road that led from the hotel to the station had not been tarred, Siane recalled ruefully as the truck bumped and lurched over the uneven track. Within minutes her slender body felt quite shaken up. Just when she was beginning to wonder if she would survive the ride the track must have emerged on to the main road, and the passage of the vehicle smoothened.

Siane lifted the corner of the canvas and took a few breaths of fresh air. The most difficult test had been passed—André Connors had not discovered her presence. Now she could set about making herself more comfortable, but she had to remain lying down. Though the road was smooth the feel of metal beneath her head was unpleasant. A pillow would be welcome. She thought of her wedding-dress. It was securely wrapped in a bag of clear plastic and she could rest her head on it without spoiling the dress.

Cautiously she rearranged her possessions. The suitcase remained in the corner; the wedding-dress beneath her head. As for the carton of cookies, which was rolling about most alarmingly, she would hold it in her arms as she lay.

Lying back beneath the canvas, with her head pillowed on the dress, she wondered what John and her parents would say if they could see her now. Mom would be horrified, Dad would be amused. As for John, he would be a bit of both; sorry that she had undergone the ordeal for his sake, but amused at her inventiveness.

What a tale this would be to tell to her grand-children! She smiled to herself in the darkness. That alone made her daring worth while.

Considering the nature of the vehicle, the ride was now surprisingly smooth. Beneath the canvas it was warm and dark and musty, and Siane was filled with a pleasant drowsiness. She would *not* sleep, she resolved. She would stay awake and alert, so that when the time came to disembark she would know exactly what she must do. But wakefulness was well-nigh impossible. Without knowing it, she slid slowly into sleep.

She came awake very suddenly. Sunlight dazzled her eyes and for a few moments she had no idea where she was. There was an unfamiliar hardness beneath her back, and her legs were dangling in the strangest way. She rubbed sleep-sticky eyes with the back of a hand, and then managed to open them properly.

A gasp of horror as she looked up. Grey eyes, gleaming with mockery, looked down at her from a face just inches away from her own. One muscled arm was hard beneath her back; the other was under

her knees, supporting her legs. Against her cheek
was the strength of a broad chest.

For a moment she lay quite still, her heart thump-
ing wildly against her ribs, her limbs assailed by a
weakness which made it impossible to move. Wide
blue eyes stared helplessly into wolfish grey ones, and
a small pink tongue went out to lick lips that were
suddenly dry.

The inertia lasted no more than a second, then
she was struggling away from him. But his arms
tightened, thwarting her attempts to stand, and
when she looked at him again she saw that the
mockery in his eyes had deepened.

'Let me down!' she snapped.

'When I'm ready to.'

Something in his tone sent a flicker of fear shivering through her. Her eyes skittered from his to take
in her surroundings. On all sides stretched the bushveld. From her vantage point she could see not a
single sign of human existence. She was completely
in the man's power, and from the wicked light in his
eyes it was clear that he knew it. It was time to be
assertive. However frightened she was, it was important that he should not know it.

'Let me down at once!' The words were said with
as much authority as was possible in the circumstances.

'Stowaways don't give orders.' His tone was insolent, bringing a flush to her cheeks and increasing
her fear.

It was not easy to swallow through the dryness at

the back of her throat. 'This one does,' she declared with as much spirit as she could muster.

'I think not.' There was a chuckle, low and sensuous, and so close to her that she could feel his breath fan her hot cheek. 'This stowaway has placed herself at my mercy, and as such will take the punishment I mete out.'

His mouth was on hers before she could twist away from him. His lips were hard, crushing hers mercilessly. Her fevered brain warned her to get away from him. Small fists balled against his chest, but the effect was only to have him pull her closer towards him, his arms holding her so tightly that she could feel the warmth of his fingers through the thin fabric of her sweater.

His head lifted quite suddenly. Grey eyes were hard and a little bleak as they studied the small flushed face, taking in the untidy tumble of dark curls, and the confusion in blue eyes, and the pulse throbbing rapidly at the base of a slender throat. 'You can stand up now,' he commanded harshly, and in the same moment he dropped the hand that supported her knees.

Only a supreme effort of will kept her legs from buckling as her feet touched the ground. She looked up at him, and then quickly away, letting long thick lashes hide the sudden rush of tears. Though the brutal embrace had been no more than a punishment, the moments in his arms had left her shaken and uncertain and at the same time more excited than she had ever been.

'I'm ... I'm sorry,' she whispered. 'I suppose I shouldn't have done it.'

'A little late for apologies.' His voice was curt.

Remorse vanished at his manner. She blinked back the tears and jerked her head up defiantly. 'Was it so wrong?'

'I'll let you answer the question.' His gaze swung over her, lingering insolently on the soft feminine curves beneath the figure-hugging sweater.

'You refused when I asked you. . . .'

'So you decided to come anyway.' An autocratic lift of an eyebrow. 'Do you always make things go the way you want them?'

She would *not* let his arrogance reduce her to the level of a chastised schoolgirl! 'When I'm in the right,' she said haughtily.

There was an odd expression in the rugged features. 'I knew last night that I'd be doing John a favour if I left you behind.'

Her head came up slowly. 'Why do you hate me so much?' she asked low-toned.

'Hate?' A dismissive shrug of the shoulders. 'You flatter yourself, Miss O'Brien. Hatred is an emotion which needs a degree of enthusiasm. I don't hate you.' A wicked flash of white teeth in the tanned face as he noted that the barb had found its target. 'Let's just say that I don't like to see a fine man's life being ruined.'

Anger surged through her, white-hot and violent. 'You think I encouraged that fellow in the lounge yesterday. What do you think I am, Mr Connors? A tart?'

'No more than the rest of your sex, Miss O'Brien.' His eyes were hard and jeering. 'Most of you will use a man to get what you want.' He paused, and she wondered what had happened in the life of André Connors to make him hold all women in such contempt. 'As far as John is concerned, I don't think a wilful little spitfire has a place in his life.'

She caught her breath at the brutality of his words. He was watching her, his gaze speculative as it touched her flushed face. Clearly he expected an outburst. But an outburst would get her nowhere. Any sarcasm on her part would only result in more insults spoken in that hard expressionless voice which was becoming rapidly familiar. Far more effective than verbal retaliation was silence and a measure of dignity.

Without a word she turned away and went to the back of the truck. One hand was on the wedding-dress, the other on her suitcase, when a voice said from behind her, 'The outraged virgin is packing her things.'

'Isn't that what you want?' she asked thickly.

'What I want seems to have become irrelevant.' His eyes were narrow as he watched her walk from the truck with as much dignity as her three pieces of luggage would allow. 'I wonder where you think you're going.'

'Back to the hotel. Where I'll wait for Friday's bus.' She refused to look at him. 'I will still get to

Crocodile View, Mr Connors.'

'I'm beginning to doubt it.' Did she imagine the hint of amusement in his tone? She shot him a swift glance, but his eyes were bland. Have you any idea where we are, Miss O'Brien?'

'Not exactly,' she replied loftily. 'But you don't need to worry about me, Mr Connors. I'll find my way.'

'John really is taking on quite something.' This time there was no mistaking the amusement. There was also another quality in his tone, something which she could not define but which made her pulses quicken. And then his hands were taking her possessions from her to put them back in the truck, and as his fingers touched hers an electric tingling quivered through her system.

'The hotel is fifteen miles back along the road.' His tone was so dry that she wondered if he had any inkling of the reaction his touch had provoked.

'We ... we've gone so far?' she asked in dismay.

'You had a long sleep atop that wedding-dress, little spitfire.' He paused. 'Get in the truck.'

CHAPTER THREE

SHE looked at him uncertainly. 'You mean you'll take me with you?'

'You took away my freedom of choice when you stowed away.' He grinned suddenly. There were specks of warm light in the greyness of his eyes, and for a moment she thought he looked almost human. 'Even I can't let a desirable young woman wander alone through the bushveld.'

'You find me desirable?' The words were out before she could stop them. Horrified, she clapped a hand over her mouth.

'You want me to prove it to you?' he drawled.

'No!' she drew herself up to her full height. 'Before I get into the truck let's make one thing quite clear. You will not lay a hand on me.'

'I told you already that stowaways don't make the rules.' A sardonic grin curved the corners of his mouth. 'You come with me on *my* terms, Miss O'Brien.'

'There's no way you can make me....'

The rest of the sentence was stifled as two hands seized her shoulders and drew her roughly to him. This time her reflexes were quicker, and as she moved her head away from the descending mouth one hand went up to strike him. But if Siane was quick, André Connors was quicker still. And he had strength on his side. A hand seized hers and forced it down, holding it pressed between her body and his. His other hand went to the back of her head, knotting through the tangle of untidy curls. Now there was no more escaping. His lips closed on hers, deliberately, firmly, staking a claim to which he had no right. Her mind rebelled at the outrage, but as he began to explore the soft sweetness of her mouth her senses reeled with an agonising delight, so that she could no more help responding than a thirsty man could have stopped drinking until his glass was empty. With her mouth imprisoned, his hands left their hold of her hair and her wrist and began a tantalising exploration of her body. She felt them sliding from her throat to her shoulders, and down her back to her hips. The hold on her hips became firmer as he pulled her towards him, moulding the feminine softness against his own angular lines so that she could feel every inch of his hard bones and taut-muscled thighs.

All thought of escape fled her mind as fierce flames of desire were ignited in her nerve-stream, a desire that was so strong that quite without volition her body arched towards his and her arms went up around his neck.

He put her from him with an abruptness which left her dazed, and for some reason bereft. She stared up at him, unaware of the tears that trembled on her lashes. The look he gave her was enigmatic.

'Well then, spitfire, I think I've proved my point.'

'Point?' she echoed, bemused.

'That the journey will be entirely on my terms.'

For a while, in those time-stopping moments when each one of her senses had reacted to his overpowering maleness, she had forgotten the purpose of his lovemaking. There had been only the pain and the rapture. The crisp statement brought it all back to her with humiliating finality. In that moment she hated him.

'You have brute strength on your side,' she said flatly. 'That makes it easy to set the terms.'

She was about to climb into the back of the truck when she heard his chuckle close behind her. Perhaps it was just that her nerves were still fragile, but the sound had a husky seductiveness which made her shiver.

'You'll sit beside me.'

'I prefer to continue as I began,' she said stiffly, refusing to look at him.

'And hand you over to your beloved shocked and bruised? Come on, spitfire,' authority appeared in his tone, 'climb in front and stop arguing. You know now that I call the tune.'

'I wish you wouldn't call me spitfire, Mr Connors,' she said, when he was seated beside her and had started the engine once more.

'It goes well with your temper.' He grinned suddenly, unexpectedly. She had been about to deliver a saucy retort when she felt her heart and her pulses racing. 'See, you were just about to flare up again. Spitfire it will remain. You'll be Siane only when you're good—which isn't very often, I imagine.' Another grin. 'You will call me André. Formality is inappropriate on this kind of trip.'

You will call me André. Not 'you may' or 'I'd like it if you would ...' From André Connors' lips the simplest phrase came out in the nature of a command. And the infuriating thing was that it would never occur to him that he would be disobeyed. She glared at him. He turned, as if he knew the intensity of her feelings, and now there was mockery in his grin. Siane clamped her lips tightly together and kept silent.

For a while they drove in silence. They had nothing specific to discuss, and small-talk would have been artificial in the circumstances. Siane's thoughts were in turmoil as she stared at the passing countryside. Though she kept her eyes firmly away from him, she was acutely aware of the long lean form at her side. He was silent now, and outwardly relaxed as he concentrated on driving, and yet there emanated from him an aura of sensuousness and virility which was so strong as to be overpowering. It was an animal-like quality, wild and earthy and primeval, and though Siane sat as far away from him as she could, her maddened senses could not help responding to his proximity.

How far away from Crocodile View was the farm where André lived? Near enough, evidently, for him to have struck up a friendship with John, yet still far enough, she fervently hoped, that her meetings with him would be seldom. She could not bear it if she had to see him often. It would be more than she could do to keep up a façade of politeness. For one thing, the moment she had set eyes on the man she had taken a violent dislike to him. For another, she would never be able to face him without re-membering his lovemaking and her own abandoned responses.

It was the last thought which disturbed her the most. She was on her way to marry the man she loved. She would never have believed that she, Siane O'Brien, was capable of being so affected by any man other than John. John's kisses had been a joy. She had missed his touch in the year that they had been apart. But while she had loved him for his tender gentleness, she knew that she had never been stirred as she had been today. It shocked her that she could have allowed her senses to get the better of her, and yet at the same time she was excited by what had happened. She could think the worst of André Connors, she could revile him to his face and in her mind, but she could not deny to herself that she had never in her life felt more vibrantly alive than in the moments when his hands and lips had caressed her.

It said something for Siane's strength of will that she was able to drag her thoughts away from the man at her side and focus her eyes on the country-side, but once she did so she found herself fasci-nated. She had known that the Eastern Transvaal would be beautiful. John had described it often in his letters, particularly in the earlier ones.

She could acknowledge now that Wilgespruit had been a disappointment. Admittedly she had seen it only when the storm was upon it, but even in good weather she could not imagine that it would be very attractive. And yet the dot on the map had been so near to the location of Crocodile View....

The scenery was very different from the bleakness of the previous day. Some time during the miles she had slept away, they had emerged from flatness into hilly country. They were on a mountain pass now, a stretch of road that snaked from slope to slope in long fluid bends. With a less experienced driver Siane might have had her nervous moments, but André drove with a quiet competence which took her mind off any possible dangers and allowed her to enjoy the breathtaking views which changed in their aspect at every bend. On one side rose the mountains, on the other, far below, were valleys, a patchwork of varying shades of green and yellow and brown. They emerged from the pass, and as the truck swept along the straight tarred road there were fields, lush with lucerne, with tobacco and citrus. There was so much cultivation that Siane wondered how far they were from Crocodile View.

When André stopped the truck she looked at him puzzled. He did not speak but jerked a hand forward in a terse gesture. Then he opened his door and got out of the truck.

In a moment Siane had taken in the position. They had come to a flooded bridge, water gushed over it, fast and deep. So deep that the truck could not negotiate it with safety?

Her eyes were drawn to the rigid line of André's shoulders. Without thinking she opened her door and ran to his side.

'Trouble?' Her eyes were on the face which had in no manner acknowledged her presence.

'As you see.' He spoke briefly, his eyes narrowed and assessing.

'The truck will make it,' Siane said confidently. She added the mental note that the driver's competence would see them safely over the bridge.

'You are an expert?' There was a jeering note as he turned to her for the first time.

She was unable to prevent the flush which swept her cheeks, but she managed to meet his gaze. 'I wouldn't have thought a bit of water would stop you.'

'It wouldn't stop you.' There was a hard edge to his tone. 'I've no doubt your impulsiveness takes you straight into any situation, before you've stopped to think whether it's safe or not.'

'You ... you really think it mightn't be safe?' she asked uncertainly, ignoring his sarcasm for the moment.

'Can't say till I've tested it.'

She remained silent as she watched him break a branch from a nearby tree. Swiftly he trimmed it, then went back to the bridge. The set look on his face as he returned to her told her all she needed to know.

'It isn't safe?'

'No.'

She thought for a moment. 'There's another way?'

'There's always another way in life.' Unexpectedly his teeth gleamed white in an unholy grin.

She looked at him warily. 'A detour?'

'If that's what you call an extra two hundred miles.'

'Impossible!' she exclaimed, the thought flashing through her mind that it was already so late that another two hundred miles would make it impossible for them to reach their destination before nightfall.

'You have another suggestion?' Grey eyes flicked her sardonically.

'You could take a chance and go over the bridge.'

'No dice.' It was said quietly but with a firmness that was enough to daunt even Siane's irrepressible spirit.

She looked at him uncertainly a few moments, small white teeth chewing at a still-bruised lower lip. 'You're worried about me,' she said at length.

'You flatter yourself, spitfire.' There was insolence in the regard which swept blatantly over the small rigid figure. 'Stowaways don't deserve consideration. What concerns me is my machinery.'

'Machinery?' Amazing that she could keep her tone so normal when her hand was itching to reach up and slap him.

'Beneath the canvas.' A terse gesture. He began to walk towards the truck. 'Let's go, spitfire.'

'No....' She ran after him, putting a small hand

on his arm to detain him. 'I've an idea.'

He looked down at her curiously. 'Let's hear it.'

'I could walk in front of the truck, show you the way. . . .' He was so quiet that a spark of hope rose inside her. 'I could do it, André, I know I could!'

'You wouldn't be frightened?' There was an enigmatic quality in the steady gaze.

'No!' And then, more slowly, 'Well, yes, just a little. But I'd do it.'

'I think you would.' Something came and went in the dark grey eyes, something she could not define but which made her pulses beat a little faster. 'It's still no go. Come along, Siane.'

He had called her Siane, not spitfire. In some way she had pleased him. The use of her name, together with the odd expression when he had said it, filled her with a satisfying warmth.

It was only when they had travelled back a little way along the road they had come, that a new thought struck her. 'Didn't you know the bridge would be flooded?' Odd how the idea that she had been wrong in her assessment of the man disturbed her. She would not have imagined him to be ignorant of road conditions.

'No. The fellow back at the inn said it would be passable.'

'You must have known there'd been a lot of rain.'

His eyes moved from the road to rest thoughtfully on the small intent face. 'Of course. But I've been away for over a week. I took him at his word when he said the river had stopped flooding.'

She could hardly argue with that. Just as she could not argue with his decision not to press on over the bridge. There was no questioning André Connors' toughness. Despite her annoyance at the fact that the journey would now be prolonged, she understood that it was a measure of the man's maturity that he tempered toughness with an ability to make calculated decisions.

Back along the highway they went, and Siane was just wondering whether they would reach Wilgespruit before dusk when the truck left the tar and turned on to a side-road. She looked at André for explanation as the vehicle bumped over the rutted country trail.

'This is the detour?'

He nodded, and she saw the lifting at the corners of his mouth. 'Be glad you're not under the canvas. What sort of pillow would the wedding-dress be now?'

She had not needed the question to make her realise how uncomfortable she would be at the back of the truck. His sarcasm was unnecessary. The man was insufferable! she thought resentfully. For a few moments, when they had left the bridge, she had thought him almost human. But it was her first assessment of André Connors which had been the correct one. He was tough, arrogant, domineering. She had no doubt at all that he could be utterly savage and ruthless when the occasion demanded.

His eyes were on the road, yet she felt that he sensed every one of the thoughts flitting through her mind. She suppressed a shudder. He should *not* know that his riling had the power to reach her.

'It would make a good pillow,' she said suddenly, defiantly, though some moments had elapsed since he had asked the question.

'What it is to be a child and to have beautiful dreams!' He chuckled, the sensuousness which was becoming rapidly familiar setting her nerves on edge. 'See that you behave yourself, spitfire, or you might still end up under the canvas again.'

Back to the nickname once more. Oddly she was beginning to like it, just a little, but there was no reason why he should know it. She turned to the window, fixing her eyes on the scenery. Tobacco fields stretched from the road, an undulating green all the way to the distant horizon.

It was beautiful countryside, but transcending the beauty was a vast and awesome loneliness. Not a tractor to be seen, not a farmer, nor even a herdsman. Just once there was another vehicle, a dilapidated horse-drawn cart with an ancient-looking man holding the reins.

In a few hours it would be nightfall. Where on this road would there be an inn where they could spend the night? And what would John say when he knew that she had been alone with André? He would be understanding, that much she knew, but he would also be concerned that she had done something so foolhardy as to stow away. Not for the first time she told herself that she must try to curb her impulsiveness.

The road grew more rutted, and the likelihood of a village with an inn became alarmingly more remote. Siane could feel tension building inside her. Twice she looked at André, she moved her lips, trying to find a way to frame a question which was really very simple. Both times she turned back to the window without speaking. Simple the question might be, but André would answer it with a sarcasm to which she would have no answer and which, she knew instinctively, would leave her feeling more vulnerable than before. She would have to wait and see where he took her. Only then could she make her decisions.

The scenery began to change once more as the road made a turn, and the mountains came into sight again, tall and misty and translucent in the distance. The afternoon was dwindling. Lengthening shadows lay across the fields, and still no village was in sight. Siane's apprehension grew. There had been no conversation between André and herself since the interchange about the wedding-dress, but now and then she felt his eyes upon her and was conscious of his perceptive amusement.

The sun was setting when he stopped the truck and opened his door. He looked across the seat at Siane, his eyes dark and sparkling.

'He just wants to stretch his legs,' she thought wildly. 'There could be no other reason why he would stop in the middle of nowhere.' But her heart skipped a beat as she saw him switch off the engine.

'An odd place to stop.' She kept her voice as controlled as she could.

'Really?' he asked lazily. 'I think it's rather a good choice.' He gestured towards a clump of willows which she had not noticed before. 'There's even a supply of running water for baths and tea.'

'You can't ... can't mean. ...' The words choked in her throat.

'We're spending the night here, little one.' The laziness had deepened. 'Get out and stretch your legs.'

'No!' Her voice rang with defiance. 'I will *not* spend the night here!'

Well-shaped eyebrows rose. 'You know of a better place?'

'A hotel. With two separate rooms.'

'No such luxury in this neck of the woods, spitfire.' André's tone was calm and relaxed. Siane guessed that he was deriving enormous satisfaction from her distress at the situation.

'John will be furious,' she ground out low-toned.

'I reckon that's between you and your loved one,' came the cool answer. 'You didn't consult me before dumping yourself in my truck.' Before she could draw breath to answer, he added, 'I'd like to stretch my legs before supper. If you're coming with me, spitfire, better get moving.'

Siane could see that he would neither wait for her, nor give in to her wishes, for already he was moving away from the truck. Swiftly she opened her door and went to join him. Her legs *did* feel cramped after the hours of driving, and much as she resented having to be in his company, it was preferable to remaining alone. He said nothing as she fell into step beside him, but the brief gaze he bestowed on her revealed that he had known she would not stay alone in the truck.

With the truck's engine switched off, they were enveloped in an all-encompassing silence, a silence so intense that it was almost tangible. Once a bird flew overhead, uttering a cry that sounded so loud as to seem shocking. It wheeled and dipped, then soared out of sight, leaving only the silence and the frightening vastness of the veld.

In contrast to the stillness all around her, Siane's mind was a chaotic whirl of thoughts. It was unthinkable that she should spend the night alone with André Connors. Not because of what John might say—she had already decided that her fiancé would be understanding, and nobody else would ever learn of it—but for another reason, one which concerned André himself. It had to do with his earthiness, with the primitive sense of power and virility which seemed to be with him at all times. She shot him a quick sideways glance, and as always his tallness surprised her, as did the toughness and ruggedness of his appearance. If only she were not quite so aware of him! Siane thought despairingly. If she could shake off the feeling of being vulnerable and at the same time vibrantly alive. . . .

Far from any sign of civilisation she would be entirely at his mercy. Would he make a pass at her?

In one sense the answer was no. She remembered the encounter with Mr Kruger, and the manner in which André had rescued her from the man's lust.

In another sense the answer could only be yes. Twice already she had felt the weight of his body against hers, and when she licked her lips she could taste the tender spot where he had bruised her. And yet neither of his embraces could be termed a pass in the ordinary sense of the word. Both had been a form of punishment, André's inimitable way of teaching her a lesson. More than ever Siane realised that she would have to be very careful.

They were making towards the willows. Siane assumed that here would be the running water André had mentioned. They came to a stream. The water was flowing swiftly, clear and sparkling so that every pebble on the stony bed was plainly visible.

A path ran along the stream, broadening here and there to a wide spread of rocks. They stopped at a point where a waterfall fell to a pool, and Siane gazed at it enchanted. It was certainly unexpected, hidden by a natural barrier of cliff and trees. She was surprised when André bent down to dash some water over his cheeks and brow.

'It's safe?' she asked.

'Perfectly.' The face that was raised to hers was a handsome mask of burnished wet bronze. 'Try it.'

'There's no bilharzia?' The clear water held an invitation that was irresistible, but still Siane hung back, aware that many streams and pools in the Transvaal were infested with the snails that bore the parasites carrying the dreaded disease.

'None.' At his sudden smile her heart seemed to miss a beat. 'You're quite right to be wary. Bilharzia is a scourge all over the province and I'm glad that you know it. But this is one stretch of water that's completely clear.'

She did not question him further as she bent to the water. Whatever her personal feelings for André Connors, she did not doubt that he was sure of his facts, nor that he would take no unnecessary risks. How she knew this was something she could not have explained, but know it she did.

The feel of the cold water on her face and hands was delicious. When they left the stream at last and wandered back along the road through the fading light Siane felt exhilarated. She was also conscious of a feeling of hunger.

'I'm starving, André!' She darted him a mischievous glance from blue eyes fringed with long spiky lashes. 'I hope the nearest restaurant has a king-sized steak.'

'You're the most demanding stowaway I ever met.' A hand went out to cup her throat, and as he drew her face up so that he could look at her, she felt the mischief vanish from her eyes. There was nothing hard in his fingers. If anything it was the tantalising lightness on the vulnerable hollows at the base of her neck which sent the adrenalin pumping through her veins.

'I am?' she managed through a parched throat.

'Also the most beautiful.' He added the words

lightly, but the bleakness in his expression took away any pleasure she might have gained from the remark.

Grey eyes, hard and implacable, stared into blue ones, which were wide and suddenly a little scared.

'I'm starving,' Siane said again, this time in an effort to restore some normality to a situation which was fast slipping beyond her control.

'You really do bear a likeness to the princess sleeping on the pea.' His glance held a taunt. 'Granted, you took the roughness of the ride very well. But you feel people have to serve you as of right.'

She flinched away from the hold on her throat. As her eyes jerked to his once more, she could feel the colour receding from her face, and she wondered why he disliked her so much.

'Why do you hate me?' The question tumbled out in a rush.

'You enjoy melodrama.' The indifference in his tone was insulting. 'I don't hate you, spitfire—I told you that yesterday.'

'But you don't consider me a suitable wife for John.' An emotion she did not understand made her tone low and husky.

'Precisely.' He paused, an odd expression in his face as he noted her indignation. 'Keep your claws sheathed, little kitten. Nothing you say will change my opinion. Now what shall it be—corned beef or wieners?'

CHAPTER FOUR

'WIENERS,' she said in a voice which was not quite steady.

Siane was trembling as she watched him walk to the truck. So André carried with him a stock of emergency rations. For some reason this further sign of his practicality made her even angrier than if there had been no food at all. He was too sure of himself, too self-sufficient, entirely too much in control of the situation. It occurred to her that André Connors would be in control of anything that touched his life; his truck, his horse, a stowaway who had managed for a brief time only to get the better of him, his women. Women.... She was aware of an odd breathlessness. There must have been many women in the life of André Connors; there always would be—his confident lovemaking made that clear. A new thought struck her. He could be married.... Briefly, quite without meaning to, Siane wondered what it would be like to be André's wife. As the thought became conscious she pushed it deliberately away. She frowned, shrugging her shoulders in an elaborate gesture of unconcern. One could only pity any girl who was foolish enough to become his wife.

As she watched him make a small fire—his hands

working with the same confidence as when they had moved over her body—she thought again how little she knew of him. He lived and worked on a farm somewhere near Crocodile View. Did he own a farm? It was difficult to imagine André Connors being subordinate to another man. And if so, what did he do there?

Tomorrow she would be at Crocodile View. Whatever she wanted to know John would tell her. If she was still interested. . . . For surely once she saw John there would be the excitement of their reunion, their plans for a speedy wedding. André Connors would lose all significance other than that of being the man who had, unwillingly, brought John his bride.

But tomorrow seemed a long way distant. It was as if the moments beside the crackling twigs were the only reality, an island of time with no beginning and no ending. Impatiently Siane shook her head. The accumulation of the day's events was making her fanciful.

André looked up quite suddenly, catching her off her guard. The pale light of the fire caused a shadow to fall across his face, giving him the appearance of a primeval man, rakish and attractive and with a primitive earthiness that was so devastating that it made Siane feel weak at the knees. Perhaps he guessed something of her thoughts, for she saw the corners of his mouth lift in a grin that was both wicked and amused. Then he said, 'Dinner is served, spitfire.'

'Th—thank you,' she said breathlessly.

'Such formality all of a sudden.' The mockery in his voice did not extend to his expression. It was too dark to see his eyes, but she had the feeling that they were quiet and watchful.

'Not formal,' she said in a composed tone that was quite at variance with the racing of her pulses. 'Just polite.'

'And is it politeness that makes you sit like a prim virgin as far from me as you can manage?' A flash of white teeth in the darkness. 'Odd, spitfire, but I could swear that you're scared of me.'

'André Connors!' She drew herself up as much as five feet four of outraged femininity could manage. 'You are the most insufferable man I've ever met!'

'Have you been associating with such a mealy-mouthed bunch, then?' There was no repentance in his tone. 'Don't answer, spitfire, you'll only get yourself into more trouble. Do you like the wieners?'

'I'll probably choke on them,' she muttered fiercely, and shivered as the low chuckle sounded in the darkness.

The horrible man and his horrible food! she thought vengefully as she bit fiercely into a wiener. Were she not so hungry she would refuse to let a morsel cross her lips. But she had had nothing to eat since the previous night and her hunger was a very real thing.

The meal was delicious. Despite her animosity towards André, she could not help enjoying the food he had prepared. The fire had given the tinned wieners a flavour she had never tasted before. There was sweet corn, warm and creamy, and afterwards, with a mug of steaming coffee, a piece of sweet konfyt. André Connors was a resourceful man, Siane acknowledged with grudging respect.

The African sunset is spectacular, but once the sun has dipped beneath the horizon it gets dark very quickly. There had been a smidgin of light when they started the meal, but that had now vanished. The sky was vast and dark and already the first stars were pricking the blackness. The great stillness of the afternoon was replaced with the shrill buzzing of the night insects. It had been hot during the day, but now Siane could feel the chill of evening hovering just beyond the reaches of the dying flames. She shivered as she hugged her sweater more tightly around her.

'Cold?' asked a voice through the darkness.

'A little,' she admitted.

They were the first words spoken since the interchange at the beginning of the meal. There had been no moment when Siane had not been acutely aware of the taut dark shape just a few feet from her. Even when he was silent André radiated a virile maleness that was almost tangible.

'I think we should start thinking of bed.' The statement was matter-of-fact, but Siane's senses quickened to immediate tension.

'Where will we sleep?' She tried to keep the tremor from her voice.

'In the truck.' He sounded amused. 'You have other ideas?'

'Yes.' She took a deep breath. It was important that she make a stand. She must speak authoritatively, from a position of strength. 'It's obvious that we can't both spend the night in the truck.'

'If you want to sleep in the open that's your privilege.' The mildness in his tone was deceptive. 'Personally, I'd find it a bit cold.'

'Not in the open,' she faltered. 'But the canvas.... André, you could sleep in the back....'

'Not a chance, spitfire.' His voice was flat. 'I intend sleeping inside.'

'But . . . but that's impossible!' Authority deserted her as she began to realise fully the implications of the situation. 'I'm going to be inside.'

'Really?' Did she imagine the laughter beneath the laziness of his tone? 'Then it would seem we'll keep each other company.'

'No!' Hysteria bubbled in her throat. 'I insist that you stay out of the truck.'

'Listen carefully, spitfire.' An iron hand bridged the gap between them to encircle her wrist in an iron grip. 'You're a stowaway. I lay down the rules. I am sleeping inside the truck. If you know what's good for you, you'll be there too.'

'If I'm not?' Her chin rose defiantly as she struggled, unsuccessfully, to free herself from his hold.

'Then whatever happens will be your own fault.'

A shrug of unconcern. 'This is leopard country, my dear. If you want to risk tempting a leopard to taste what's no doubt very sweet flesh, that's up to you.'

She swallowed hard to suppress a shudder. 'You wouldn't give a damn if I was eaten, would you?'

'No,' he agreed cheerfully, 'I wouldn't give a damn.'

His hand left her wrist as he bent to the nearly-dead fire. As she watched him beating out what was left of the flames, Siane was struck by a sudden thought. He would be furious, of course, but there would be nothing he could do about the situation, and by tomorrow his anger would not matter....

'All right, then,' she said with elaborate casualness. 'Since there's nothing for it. You'll give me a few minutes alone, won't you?'

'Will you sound so plaintive on your wedding-night?' She knew he was mocking her, but she managed to keep silent—no point in angering him prematurely. 'Run along, spitfire, and make yourself decent.'

He could keep his sarcasm, Siane thought exultantly, as she walked quickly to the truck, trying not to look at the shadows cast by the few sparse trees. How he would curse her, but for once there would be nothing he could do about it. She would have the upper hand, she had outwitted him.

She held her breath as she climbed into the truck. Yes! The keys were in the ignition, just as she had remembered. Letting out her breath, she gave a quiet exclamation of glee. It took no more than a moment to lock both doors. Then she settled back in her seat and waited.

Leopard country.... André Connors would stop at nothing to frighten her or cause her discomfort, but it could also be true. This was the bushveld. Crocodile View could not be very far distant, and in the game park predators roamed. And beyond Crocodile View lay the Kruger National Park, just a little further away on the map. Did the parks have fences? Siane didn't know. One read occasionally of farmers who had problems with a stray lion or leopard. But it didn't happen often. And they went usually for cattle....

Siane felt hot as conscience pricked her. Should she unlock the doors and let him in? No! André would be perfectly safe beneath the canvas, and it would surely be an abnormal leopard which would pick up his scent.

A hand tried the door on the driver's side. Siane watched with a scared fascination as the handle jerked up twice more. She had expected the rap at the window, but it came with such force that she flinched.

'Open the door, spitfire!'

'No,' she said, and giggled when she realised that he couldn't hear her.

Tensely she awaited his next move. She was prepared, when his anger had cooled, to open the window just a fraction, so that she could hand him what he needed for the night. She turned her head, searching for any warm clothing lying around. He should not be able to accuse her of callousness. By tomorrow he might even have had time to understand that she had taken this step because....

A rude shattering of her thoughts as the door on the driver's side was jerked open. Siane shrank back terrified. There was something ominous about the long body which inserted itself unhurriedly into the truck.

'H-how did you get in?' she asked through quivering lips.

He turned to her, and in the light that shone from the ceiling of the vehicle she saw that his face was pale and dangerous. 'A spare set of keys, my dear.' And then, when he had closed the door, 'I pity John. You don't possess a single scruple in that infinitely attractive little body.'

'I do.' She blinked back her tears. 'Th-that's just it. I ... I didn't want to sleep with you....'

'With?' he questioned. 'Alongside was what I had in mind. But perhaps it's "with" that you're angling for?'

'Don't you touch me!' she snapped, withdrawing as far as she could to her side of the seat.

A mirthless chuckle. 'Why not?'

This was *the* most ridiculous conversation she had ever had. She swallowed hard. 'Because I don't want you to.'

'I wonder if you really know what you want?' The outrageous drawl sent a quiver through her nervestream.

'Of course,' she said, and wished that her voice showed more conviction.

'I wonder, spitfire.'

There was no time to open the door and make for the relative safety of the darkness outside. An arm shot along the seat behind her, gripping her shoulders and pulling her across his lap. His head came down slowly, deliberately. She waited breathlessly, making no effort to fight him. The thought crossed her mind that if she was docile he would lose his taste for battle. His lips touched her eyes, her ears, pausing to nibble at an ear-lobe, then sliding down her neck to the pulsing hollow at the base of her throat. They were lips that teased and tantalised, tasting and exploring with a sensuous life of their own. Upwards they went again, and now, when they came to rest on her lips, the teasing lightness was gone. As her lips parted beneath his, and the pressure became merciless, she was pulled roughly closer. The other hand went to her sweater, pushing it upwards, sliding over the bare skin till it found the roundness of a firm breast.

Now there was no more thought of escape, no rational thought of any kind. There was only the world of the senses. The feel of taut thighs beneath her back, the beat of a strong heart against her chest. As the mobile lips ravished her mouth, Siane was aware of the moan that escaped her. Her body was alive with a flaming agony of desire such as she had never before experienced, and there was only the wish to be closer to him, and still closer....

When he raised his head she was conscious only of disappointment. Her breathing was ragged, her pulses in turmoil. She stared at him wide-eyed, totally unable to speak, to move.

'Well, spitfire.' His voice was so normal that it came as a shock. Only his slightly heightened breathing indicated that he had been in any way affected by what had happened between them. 'Now do you know what you want?'

Anger surged through her—anger at the insolence of his tone, and, even more, at her unbridled response to his lovemaking.

'Yes!' she hissed through clenched teeth. 'I want you to keep out of my way. If you think I'd let you sleep with me you were never more mistaken!'

'You do want it, my dear. Your response just now proved it.' His laugh was mocking, dismissive. 'If there was a bed at hand I might just consider the matter. But as it happens, sleeping with a child on the seat of a truck is not my scene.'

Anger lent her strength. Now she was able to lever herself from his lap. She was shaking as she moved back to her side of the seat. 'There will never be a bed for you and me, André Connors. You'd better believe it.'

'I believe that at least you know now what you want,' he said cryptically. He reached for a blanket —vaguely she remembered that he had brought it with him into the truck. Another emergency measure? 'It's going to be a long night, and a cold one. Sorry there's only one blanket, but it'll cover us both.'

She sat stiff and unresisting while he draped half the rug over her shoulders, then covered himself with the other half. She did not reply to his 'Sleep well, spitfire.'

Her proximity did nothing to keep André awake. Within minutes he was asleep, the sound of his breathing slow and steady. It would be a long night, he had said, and as Siane gazed out into the darkness, she knew it would be just that. Last night he had disturbed her sleep with his image. Tonight he was doing it again, but in a different way. Her body still quivered with the emotions he had aroused in her. Her mind still tingled with outrage. She was intensely aware of the long male form beneath the blanket. Too aware.... If she moved just a fraction towards him her thighs would touch his. He would never know it, for he was sleeping. Yet it seemed very important that she did not touch him in any way. Even more important in the light of the quite ridiculous fact that more than anything she wanted to let her hand feel his cheek, let her fingers run through the thickness of the dark hair.

Very gently, and despite her better judgment, she raised the corner of the blanket. There was just enough light from the stars to reveal the face and form of the sleeping man. Dark hair fell carelessly across a high patrician forehead, and his features were relaxed. It was hard to imagine anyone quite as aggressively masculine as André Connors succumbing to sleep; it gave him a vulnerability which he did not possess at any other time. Yet curiously, even in repose, the sense of tautness, of sheer male virility, did not leave him.

It was not in Siane to remain angry for long. As her annoyance began to fade, so the events of the evening came back to her with a vividness that was both alarming and delightful. The memory of the strong arms moulding her body to his brought back the same ecstasy she had felt then. As if he was awake and kissing her now, she experienced again the taste of his lips, and the tingling of long lean fingers against the vulnerable swell of her breast.

With an effort she tore her eyes from the sleeping man, she let the rug fall back into place, and gazed into the darkness outside the truck. If impulse was one facet of her nature, honesty was another. She could not deny to herself the treacherous abandon with which her body had responded to André's touch, but as yet she was at a loss to explain it. Never in all her twenty-three years had she experienced anything like the mad desire which had ignited her body just a short while ago. It was frightening to think that she, who thought she knew herself so well, did not know herself at all.

What was there about the tall lean man with the bronzed body and rugged features that caused her senses to dominate her mind? She did not like him. Like? She hated him! He was arrogant and sure of himself and utterly inconsiderate of her as a person. More than that, it was inconceivable that she could allow herself to be so carried away when she was on her way to the man she loved, when the whole rigorous journey had been undertaken merely because she could no longer wait to become John's wife. Was it possible to love one man with the heart, and respond to another man with the senses? Until today she would have been positive about the answer; now she was no longer certain of anything.

Sighing deeply, she drew her portion of the rug more closely around her. She would never sleep, but at least she could try.

The first rays of the sun were streaming in through the window when she awoke. She felt stiff and cramped and uncomfortable, and her bed seemed unfamiliar. Then, as she stretched her arms and touched the front window of the truck, the events of the previous day flooded back.

She jerked her head to the side. She was alone on the seat. André was not in the truck, but the rug was tucked about her body. On waking, he must have given her his share of it. At the realisation that he had folded the rug about her sleeping form, her cheeks flamed.

She was wondering what to do next when the door at the driver's side opened and André appeared. His dark hair was wet and freshly combed, his face glowed with vigour and health, and his eyes were sparkling. He looked so handsome and vital and compelling that it was impossible for Siane to remain composed and unaffected.

'Sleep well, spitfire?' came the irreverent greeting.

'Like a log,' she flashed back at him. Not for anything would she let him know the soul-searching and the agonising he had caused her.

'Good. I've started a fire. Breakfast will be ready by the time you've had your bath.'

'Bath?' She stared at him uncomprehendingly.

'The pool I showed you yesterday.' Before she could protest, he had pulled the blanket from her shoulders. Grey eyes swept her with a gaze that was both intimate and amused. 'A crumpled-looking stowaway if ever I saw one.'

'I ... I don't have my bathing suit,' she faltered, cursing herself for the colour that rose higher beneath his scrutiny.

'I didn't have one either,' he informed her blandly. 'Get moving, spitfire. We've a long day's drive ahead of us.'

Never in all her life had she swum in the nude, and the thought of André not far away was disconcerting. But even he would not stoop to spying on her. Besides, he would be busy with the fire. Could she do it? No.... Yes! She really was crumpled, and sticky from the long night in her clothes and in the narrow confines of the vehicle. André's own glowing freshness made her feel even worse. She recalled the pool at the foot of the waterfall. The idea was tempting, too tempting....

She glanced up to find André's eyes still upon her. He looked so amused that she knew he understood the contradiction of the thoughts in her mind. She lifted her chin and met his gaze. So what if she had never swum nude in her life! This strange journey seemed to be a time for firsts.

With André's towel slung over her shoulder— the man seemed prepared for every contingency— Siane made her way to the pool. There was a lift in her step as she walked. The early morning bushveld had a strange and haunting beauty. Veld flowers peeped through the scrub beside the road, a mixture of yellow and orange and purple, so tiny that a passenger in a passing vehicle would never spot them. The tobacco plants were alive with the sheen of the sun, and nearer the stream the acacias and the mimosas radiated a spicy aroma.

How the sounds of the veld changed with the time of day, Siane mused. Yesterday, in the hour before dusk, there had been the vast stillness. Later, when darkness had fallen, the night air had been alive with the chirping of a million crickets. Now it was bird-song which filled the air.

The water was very cold. It was also delicious. Seen in the early morning light, the pool had lost none of its appeal. It was a place of secluded enchantment, with the waterfall cascading down the rocks, and the flat mossy stones at the water's edge. It was a novel experience to bathe in the nude, Siane decided, enjoying the feel of the water about her body. Some day, when she had the opportunity and there was nobody to disturb her, she would try it again. For a while she splashed and frolicked and played.

A new sound rang through the bird-song, impinging on her consciousness. A few short barks. She was startled. If there was a dog nearby, there could also be a farmer. She could not let herself be seen like this.

She was almost at the water's edge when she saw André. He was leaning against a rock. In one hand was the towel, her clothes were beneath his arm.

She thought her heart would stop. How dared he creep up on her like this! Hastily she dipped down in the water once more.

'Go away!' she shouted.

'Not a chance,' was the cheerful rejoinder.

'I want to get out. . . .' It was hard to sound commanding when she was shaking with fear and an inexplicable excitement.

'I'm waiting.'

'André. . . .' Only a heart of stone could ignore the pleading in her tone. 'I can't . . . you know that.'

'You want me to come in and get you?' The corners of his mouth had lifted, and she knew that he was mocking her once again.

'Don't you dare!' Now she managed to inject some measure of control into her tone. 'Just put down that towel and walk away like a gentleman.'

Heavens! but she would tear a strip off him when she was dry and dressed. Creeping up on her when she had thought herself unobserved! She had trusted him. For all his arrogance she had not thought he would stoop to this! If only he would go.... The water was becoming unbearably cold.

It seemed that her commands made no impression on him. André remained where he was, leaning elegantly against the rock.

The water was growing even colder and Siane's teeth were beginning to chatter. She could see that André registered her discomfort. 'Out, spitfire!' he ordered.

'If you would just put down the towel....' Tears of frustration pricked her eyelids.

'And you imagine you'd be better off that way?' There was an odd edge to his tone. She looked at him uncomprehendingly, as he jerked his head to one side.

Quite suddenly she saw them. Monkeys. Monkeys watching her, their eyes alert with mischief. The barking.... It came to her in a rush. Did monkeys bark, or were there also baboons in the trees?

'You mean....' She stopped.

'It's either me or the monkeys.' He spoke gravely, but she saw the taunt in his eyes. 'If I put down your clothes you'll have to climb the trees to get them back.'

It seemed there was nothing for it. Perhaps it was useless to appeal to his sense of chivalry and ask that his eyes be averted as she left the pool. Chivalry was a word that would not exist in the vocabulary of André Connors. But she decided to try it all the same. 'Please, André, would you look the other way?'

'You don't really need to know the answer to that,' he mocked her. 'I'd advise you to move quickly, spit-fire. If I get you to Crocodile View with pneumonia, John will have even more on his hands.' A slight pause. 'God knows, he has enough already.'

It did not occur to her to ask what he meant. There was just one thing on Siane's mind. The few steps out of the water to the refuge of the towel were the most difficult she had ever taken.

CHAPTER FIVE

SOMEHOW she did it. She could not look at André, so she did not know whether his eyes were averted, or whether he watched her running from the water, and she knew better than to ask. She thought he would leave her now, but he wrapped the towel around her and began to hug her dry. She wanted to tell him to stop, but she was trembling so violently that she could not speak.

She had never felt quite so vulnerable as she did now, with the big towel around her body and the compelling maleness so potent that it threatened to overwhelm her. Tears were trembling on her lashes, and she did not want him to see them. With an instinctive gesture she turned her head and hid it somewhere in the region of his chest.

She thought she heard him murmur 'brave girl', and wondered if she imagined that his lips had touched her wet hair. His hands were firm and strong. Through the towel they moved over her body with a sensuousness that was well-nigh unbearable. It came to her that he was like a sorcerer of old, moulding her, shaping her to his whims. If she did not break free quickly she would be forever under his spell. She lifted her head to look at him, and encountered the steady gaze of grey eyes that were narrowed and watchful.

'You're no gentleman,' she said bitterly, ignoring the voice inside her that bade her be still and enjoy the moment.

'Are you a lady?' he countered derisively. 'Locking me out of my truck was not the most honourable of actions.'

'So I'm being punished?' For some reason the trembling had increased. Which was absurd, for by now her body had regained some of its warmth. Vaguely she was aware that the trembling had something to do with the look in his eyes, with the feel of his hands through the towel. It was a realisation she tried to push from her mind, for to acknowledge it would bring self-knowledge and the revelation of a truth which she was not ready to admit.

'Punishment?' he queried with a deceptive laziness. 'No more than you deserve. But rescue too, if you care to admit it.'

'The monkeys?' she faltered.

'They came down to the water after you were already in. I saw them running through the trees.' His glance went to the underwear which was still clamped under his arm. He grinned suddenly, and she saw the specks of light which shone through the greyness of his eyes. 'I think they found your clothing diverting.'

The lights deepened as he looked down at her, and all at once it was more than she could do than to meet that disturbing gaze. 'Let me get dressed,' she begged him low-toned.

'All right.' His arms dropped to his side. 'Breakfast will be ready in a few minutes.'

She watched him walk away through the trees. With trembling fingers she began to dress. The monkeys had retreated to a nearby tree. She saw them running along the branches, cartwheeling and looping over and under with their tails. Normally she would have found their antics amusing; if John was with her now they would be watching in a silence broken only when he whispered some explanation to her, some anatomical detail which might have escaped her.

But now, alone, she saw the antics in an abstracted kind of way. Her conscious mind was on what had just happened with André. She never would have gone swimming if she had imagined that he would see her. She had taken it for granted that he would keep his distance. Perhaps this was so because John would not have taken advantage of a girl in similar circumstances, and Siane used John as her yardstick when it came to measuring men or gauging their potential behaviour. And that was where she had been foolish. She knew already that the arrogant André was very different from the gentle John, and so she should have been prepared.

Of course, there was the matter of the monkeys. Probably the mischievous animals really would have snatched her clothes away, and then her predicament would have been all the worse. But she was not yet ready to use the monkeys as a reason to absolve André's actions. Into her mind came once more the picture of a sorcerer. She was being absurd! Or was she? Was it only because she hated the man so much that she was ready to endow him with the power of tailoring a situation according to his whims?

She was being fanciful; she knew it. André could not have lured the monkeys to the pool. But it was only when she had regained some measure of her composure that she could let herself admit the reason for her wild thoughts. Her preoccupation with the monkeys was no more than a way of pushing from her mind the thought which disturbed her even more—the matter of her own reactions.

Useless to deny that she had enjoyed the moments in his arms, when she had stood quite naked and had let him towel her dry. She had been furious, oh yes! She had found the touch of the hands through the towel maddeningly sensual. But through it all she had felt intensely feminine and deliciously excited. And she wondered again what there was about this man that he could set her senses reeling as they had never done before. Whatever was the source of his magic, it was dangerously potent.

Breakfast was a silent affair. Siane initiated no conversation of her own, and it seemed that André was not a man for small-talk The meal was simple, but surprisingly tasty—coffee and toasted rusks and long strips of dry kudu biltong. She had thought that she would eat the very minimum—perhaps he would recognise her gesture of defiance. But when she took her first sip of coffee the resolution crumbled. The swim and the crisp morning air had sharpened her appetite so that she could have eaten enough for three people.

For a while she kept her eyes down, but finally the temptation to look up was irresistible. He was watching her, his eyes filled with a familiar speculation. She sat up straighter, wrapping her cloak of dignity more tightly about her. The amusement in the grey eyes changed to insolence as they subjected her to a deliberate and intimate scrutiny. First they lingered on her face, sparkling with satisfaction as hot colour flooded her cheeks. Then came the slow descent to her throat, her shoulders, her breasts, and then downwards again, over the curves and lines of her hips and thighs. He missed nothing, not the pulse beating madly at the small exposed hollow of her throat, nor the rapid rise and fall of her breasts which was due to her quickened breathing. She was wearing jeans and a blouse, but she knew that he saw beneath the clothes to her body as it had been when she emerged from the pool. And again she wondered how much he had seen; how long he had been watching her.

When his gaze returned to her face she was ready for him. Her chin was high, and her expression had assumed as much haughty disapproval as she could muster. Whatever he had said, she *was* a lady, and he had treated her shamefully. What was more, she was another man's bride, and that man was his friend. Had he no scruples, no sense of honour whatsoever?

The glance which had been meant to wither left him undisturbed. If anything, it increased his amusement, so that it was Siane herself who was discomfited. As a long arm reached out and rumpled her hair she had to steel herself not to tremble.

'Time to get off your high horse,' he said cheerfully. 'Get the breakfast cleared, spitfire, while I see to things in the truck. It's time we were on our way.'

It was still early, and the sun was not yet high in the sky. Later it would be hot, but as yet the countryside had a look of dew-filled freshness. There were more fields of tobacco, and citrus orchards with the fruit large and brightly yellow against the dark green of the trees, and plantations where avocadoes alternated with mangoes and nuts. There were more streams, and waterfalls tumbling down high cliffs, a wonderful sight in a country where water was so sparse that many a bridge spanned only a dry river-bed. Emerging from the farm lands and the orchards, they came into timber plantations, and here Siane gazed enthralled into the forests. This was hilly country, where the trees grew straight and tall on the fertile slopes. Here and there trails led off through the forests, and neat piles of logs lay waiting for transportation to the timber mills. The road rose and fell, twisted and turned, and at each point the view was different. As the top of a rise there would be a view of the distant mountains, purpled and hazy in the morning mist, and far be-

low were valleys, a brilliant patchwork of lovely
colours.

Where did André fit into the picture? she wondered. She knew only that he was involved in farming, but she had no idea what kind. Whatever he
did, it would be efficient: somehow she knew that.
And his orders would be followed without question.
The time they had spent together had revealed that
André Connors would be subservient to no man. He
was a natural leader of men—and of women, she
had to admit a little wryly. He was a man who would
dictate and control and expect people to follow his
orders. But they would follow him willingly. The
thought came to her without volition, startling her,
so that she caught her breath and was aware of her
sudden quickened breathing. Men would follow
André, because they trusted him. As for women. . . .
Women would run to his bidding. Only Siane, impulsive, quick to anger yet quick also to laugh at
herself, felt the need to defy him. Why was she different? What made her flaunt him, when instinct
told her that he was strong and sure and that his decisions would be tempered with wisdom? It was a
quality in the man himself, she thought, something
in his personality which set a flame to her emotions
so that she clashed with him at every point.

A timber lorry was in the road in front of them,
the great load of logs causing it to sway from side to
side. The road was narrow, and the lorry made visi-
bility poor. André had to concentrate fully on driving, and Siane was able to glance at him sideways

and know that she was unobserved.

She should have known her senses would react when she looked at him. He was wearing a navy sports shirt, and against it his arms and the long strong column of his throat looked more than ever bronzed. Lean fingers held the wheel with an easy competence. At the thought of how those fingers could stir her to heights she had never thought possible, she shivered. In profile his appearance was no less arrogant than when viewed full-face. The nose was strong and well shaped, the curve of the chin was firm. Each single feature had its place in a face which was rugged and spare and stern.

For the first time she noticed the crease which ran from his nose to the edge of the mouth. Laughter lines! She wondered why she had not noticed them before. Was it because they seemed to have no place in a person who was so aggressively male? Or was it only because she had never associated André with laughter, had in fact never heard him laugh out loud? She had heard him chuckle, yes, that sensual sound which dizzied her senses. And she had seen his eyes light in an amusement which was usually mocking or derisive. But the laughter lines around his mouth suggested genuine amusement, a sense of humour and a zest for life. The laughter that went with those lines was a thing she had not yet heard. And upon that thought came another—perhaps André's laughter was reserved solely for someone else, someone special, with whom he shared not only his jokes but his dreams. She was unprepared for the tiny knife of pain which slipped between her ribs at the thought.

With greater determination than seemed necessary in the circumstances, she jerked her gaze back to her window. But the passing scenery had lost some of its charm. She was glad that André could not see the tears that pricked at her eyelids as she stared into the forests. He was everything she most detested in a man. If she now gave him the power to make her unhappy that would be unbearable.

For the last hour she had been enjoying the drive. Now she wished that the journey would end quickly. She needed John, and the refuge and sanity and happiness that only he could give her.

In the meantime, it would do no harm to show André Connors that his proximity and his sensual virility meant nothing to her. Less than nothing!

When she turned her head to look at him once more, her chin was lifted, her eyes bright, and her voice as cool as she could make it. 'How far to Crocodile View?'

'An hour.' She heard the amusement in his tone, and as he turned his head to meet her gaze—the lorry had been passed and the road was clear—she had the strangest feeling that he knew exactly the thoughts that had been passing through her mind. Which was absurd. There was no way in which he could know. And yet the feeling persisted.

'So long?'

'I thought you were enjoying the scenery.' There was derision in the glance which flicked her face, missing nothing of the brightness in her eyes and the warmth in her cheeks.

'I was ... I mean, I am.' Darn the man! What was it about him that made her feel so young and defenceless? Stiffly she said, 'The countryside is very beautiful,' and hoped that she sounded the mature woman that she was.

'It is,' he agreed, and again she realised that he was laughing at her. She was wondering how she could regain control of the situation when he asked, 'How long since you saw John?'

She looked at him uncertainly. The question was innocent enough, but there was an odd note in his tone which troubled her. 'A year.'

'And how long have you been engaged?'

'Two years—officially. But we've always known we would be married.' She hesitated. 'Why?'

'You've both waited so long that I can't help wondering why you decided to make this trip now, without even letting John know that you were coming.'

Again she stared at him. His tone had been completely without expression. There was no reason for her heartbeat to accelerate. 'What are you trying to say?' she managed at last.

The dark head turned and for a brief moment the grey eyes rested dispassionately on the small flushed face. 'Why didn't you let John know you were coming?'

'It was meant to be a surprise,' she blurted out.

'You weren't afraid that if you told John of your

plans he might put you off?'

At the cool deliberation in his tone Siane caught her breath. When she rushed back into speech she forgot to be calm and mature and considered. 'Afraid? Of John? I should say not! You're being hateful, André Connors!' A small hand lifted to dash a treacherous tear from a soft flushed cheek. 'You're implying that John doesn't want me.'

'Calm down, spitfire,' he ordered, but gently.

'I won't calm down!' she returned hotly. 'I've had only nastiness and insults from you since the moment we met. John and I are engaged. He loves me. He wants me to come.'

He was unmoved by the outburst. 'I asked you a question. Why now, Siane? Without letting him know?'

Perhaps it was the use of her name which calmed her, letting her think about the answer. 'He seemed ill,' she said at length. 'His letters ... lately.... He hasn't been himself.' And with a returning flash of spirit, 'He needs me.' Blue eyes were troubled as she searched André's face. 'Has he been ill?'

'Not that I know.' There was an odd inflection in his tone. It caught at Siane, alerting her senses, though in what way she could not explain.

Very slowly she said, 'You seem to think that John doesn't want me.'

When he spoke again she expected derision, but instead there was a strange gentleness which took her by surprise. 'Have you ever thought, Siane, that John might have other plans?'

She stared at him, unable to believe what he had said. She had known André was arrogant, had sensed his ruthlessness almost from the start. But she had not dreamed that he disliked her so intensely that he would stoop to humiliating insinuations.

'No!' Now her tone was thick with loathing. 'I haven't thought it for a moment. I love John and I trust him. It's been that way since we were children.' She shot him a look of burning defiance. 'It's the kind of relationship you wouldn't understand, André Connors. There's a smugness in you that wouldn't let you love or trust anybody but yourself.'

'You know me so well, spitfire?' There was just the slightest tightening at the corners of the mouth.

'As well as I'd ever want to know you.' She waited a moment to let her contempt sink in. Then she said, 'As far as John is concerned, I hope I've satisfied you.'

An unconcerned shrug of broad shoulders. But in his eyes, when he took them from the road for a moment, was a quality she had not seen there before. Pity? No! She rejected the thought. It could not be that, for there was no reason for it. Compassion, perhaps? Because he still thought of her as the princess sleeping on the pea and incapable of adjusting to a life of loneliness and simple basics? Or was it compassion for John, because André had taken a dislike to Siane and thought her unsuitable for his friend? Compassion for John: it had to be that.

'You don't think I'm the right wife for John, do you?'

'No,' he agreed evenly.

It was the answer she had expected, but nevertheless the uncompromising tone of the reply gave her a jolt. She should have remained silent, but something forced her to go on. 'You don't think I can take the life?'

'Not many women can.' She heard the bitterness in his tone.

'Perhaps I'm different,' she tossed at him.

'You have more spirit than most.' Mixed with the mockery there was also amusement, but when he spoke again the amusement had vanished. 'It takes a special kind of woman to live in the bushveld, Siane. Don't let the glamour fool you. In no time at all you'll be hankering for the bright lights of the city.'

'You're wrong about me. I'll prove it.' She had the feeling she was flinging down a gauntlet.

Briefly his eyes met hers once more, and again she saw the suggestion of pity. 'Will you, spitfire? I think not. But there's nothing I can say that will move you, is there? You'll barge in where you might not be wanted. And you'll insist on making mistakes that can be avoided. And you'll be surprised when you end up breaking your heart.'

She stared at him in disbelief. She knew that he wanted to hurt her, and that she must learn to harden herself against him, but still his words had the power to wound.

'Whatever happens, I won't come crying on *your* shoulder!' she threw at him blindly, and through the turmoil of her own emotions she had the satisfaction of seeing the displeasure which darkened his face.

She watched him a moment longer, seeing the hands that held the wheel with unnecessary rigidity, the tightness around the mouth and jaw, the expression which, if that was possible, had become even sterner than before. Then, with a little grimace of distaste, she turned back to her window.

Now there was no more conversation between them. Siane's stomach was a tight knot of tension. Despite her resolve not to let André's arrogance get to her, she was taut with anger. How dared André say the things he did? How dared he imply that John might not want her, when all along her fiancé had planned for the time when they would be together?

It came to her only gradually that somewhere in André's past there had been a woman who had hurt him very much. That ever since he had equated all other women with her. That this was the cause for his bitterness and his arrogance.

Slowly, very slowly, she relaxed. She did not try to speak to him again, but looked out of the window at the scenery which had changed once more. On one side of the road there were the farmlands, but on the other, there was bare veld. Real bushveld now, with the wild grass high and rough and blowing in the wind. There were trees, thorny umbrella-shaped acacias and spreading maroelas, as well as other trees whose names she did not know. This was game country, she felt it instinctively. And with a sudden excitement she knew that they were no longer far from Crocodile View.

Dignity forgotten, she turned impulsively to André. 'Crocodile View?' she asked breathlessly.

'No. But another game park.' There was no anger now in his eyes, nor derision, and his voice was quiet. 'There are several private reserves along this stretch. A little further to the right is the Kruger National Park.'

The Kruger Park.... The great South African sanctuary for wild game. Once it had been John's ambition to become a ranger there. But this job had been a tempting offer when it came. Siane wondered if life in the Kruger Park would have been very different. Less lonely perhaps, as there were so many camps, so many rangers. But loneliness would not matter when she was with John.

She sat forward eagerly, her eyes on the bush. No matter that this was not Crocodile View, it was a reserve very much like it. All was still—at least outwardly. But there were animals here, Siane knew. There were the predators, the lions and leopards and the ugly spotted hyenas. And there were the hunted, the kudu, the water antelope, the gentle impala. Here life existed as it had done for thousands of years, before man had made his inroads. It was secret, this life of the bush, hidden from the casual motorist who saw only what was at the roadside and knew nothing of signs and tracks and odours. This was the life John had chosen, and though Siane loved animals mainly for what they represented to her fiancé, she knew nevertheless that she would not find it hard to get caught up in the thrills and dangers adherent to a ranger's life.

A glint of brown showed through the trees, and as the car sped forward she saw a herd of impala grazing in a clearing. There was something so peaceful, so graceful and delicate about the scene, that she was moved to an exclamation of pleasure.

'Aren't they lovely!'

'Pretty animals,' André agreed. Something in his tone made her look swiftly at him. For a moment his eyes met hers, and in them was a look which made Siane feel all at once as if she had been childish again, and somehow naïve. She wondered why André took every opportunity to let her feel at a disadvantage.

'You prefer the lions, I've no doubt.' It was a foolish remark, and she was not certain what drove her to make it, but having begun she could not resist going on. 'They have a ruthlessness which would appeal to you.'

An eyebrow lifted sardonically, and there was a slight deepening of the line that ran from the well-shaped nose down to the edge of the mouth. 'You know me so well after just two days? Think how well you'd know me after a week.'

There was a mockery in his tone which made his meaning unmistakable. Siane cursed the colour

Could <u>you</u> dare love a man like this?

Leon Petrou was wealthy, handsome and strong-willed, and used women merely to satisfy his own desires. Yet Helen was strongly...almost hypnotically drawn to him.

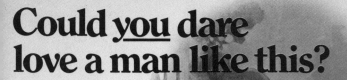

Could you dare love a man like this?

YES, eavesdrop on Leon and Helen in the searing pages of "Gates of Steel" by the celebrated best-selling romance author, Anne Hampson. She has crafted a story of passion and daring that will hold you in its spell until the final word is read.

You'll meet Leon, Helen and others, because they all live in the exciting world of *Harlequin Presents*, and all four books shown here are your FREE GIFTS to introduce you to the monthly home subscription plan of *Harlequin Presents*.

A Home Subscription
It's the easiest and most convenient way to get every one of the exciting *Harlequin Presents* novels! And now, with a home subscription plan you won't miss *any* of these true-to-life stories, and you don't even have to go out looking for them. You pay nothing extra for this convenience, there are no additional charges ...you don't even pay for postage!

Fill out and send us the handy coupon now, and we'll send you 4 exciting *Harlequin Presents* novels absolutely FREE!

Harlequin Presents...

ANNE HAMPSON
Gates of steel

JANET DAILEY
no quarter asked

ANNE MATHER
sweet revenge

VIOLET WINSPEAR
devil in a silver room

Mail this coupon today!

Get your
Harlequin Presents
Home Subscription NOW!

For exciting
details, see special
offer inside.

Printed in U.S.A.

that rose swiftly to her cheeks. 'I know you as well now as I'd ever want to,' she threw at him saucily.

'You're certain of that?' The question was asked with a laziness which made it all the more outrageous, and his eyes held a taunt which sent the blood surging through her veins. This time she would not answer him, for he would only flatten her with a remark that was even more audacious, and to which she would be unable to respond.

Closing her lips tightly, she stared mutinously through the window. From close beside her came a low laugh, as if the man who drove the truck sensed her reactions. Not for the first time she told herself she was being absurd to endow him with the kind of perception he could not possibly possess. Yet even with her eyes glued to her own window, she was acutely aware of him. He had an aura which was peculiarly his own. It was a primitive thing, filling the air and enveloping the nostrils and leaving the senses reeling even when they were hardened against him.

'Get me to Crocodile View,' she pleaded silently, 'and then stay out of my life. I want nothing further to do with you.' And even as she said the words to herself, she knew they were not entirely true. A wave of self-knowledge tugged at her consciousness, but with something approaching horror she pushed it from her mind and tried to concentrate instead on the view beyond the window.

CHAPTER SIX

'SIANE....'

Had he called her Spitfire she would have ig-
nored him, but something in the way he said her
name urged her to turn.

'There!' A nod to the right. 'See them?'

'Where?' For a moment all she saw was a vast
and empty stretch of bush. And then, above the
trees, she saw great moving specks. 'Birds?' She
looked at him, a little puzzled.

'Vultures.'

'Oh!' She knew the significance of the birds of
carrion. 'They wait for a kill?' She looked at him
for confirmation. 'When the lions have had their
fill the vultures take their turn.'

'John has taught you well.' There was a strange
look in the steady grey eyes. 'Do you also know that
they attack the young and the vulnerable?'

She did not answer. No answer was called for. But
a chill ran through her system. Somehow she had
the feeling that André was referring to something
other than helpless animals. He could not mean that
a vulture would attack an adult and able-bodied
female. All the same, his words held a warning.
More than ever she longed to reach Crocodile View.

The entrance to the park lay around a bend in
the road. They came to it quite suddenly. Siane's

eyes lit up at sight of the rustic pine-logged lodge, its walls covered with a purple bougainvillea. The wooden gate was closed against strange cars, and on a pile of rocks was a jagged piece of bark bearing the words 'Crocodile View'.

André had hardly stopped the truck when the gate swung open. The gateman's wide smile seemed to indicate that André was a familiar and well-liked visitor who had no need to go through the usual formalities. Siane looked wonderingly around her as they drove on into a vista of bush stretching all the way to the horizon.

There were so many questions she longed to ask André. But always she took the risk of laying herself open to his barbs. She turned her head, and caught his eyes on her face. 'The camp is five miles down the road.' There was something unexpectedly gentle in his voice, and for some reason it unnerved her. It was as if he anticipated that she was in for a shock and was trying to help her.

She did not answer him, but bit her lip and turned back to her window. She was letting him get to her again, allowing even the most casual remark to take on an importance it did not deserve. And again she wondered what there was about the man that he should affect her so profoundly.

Whatever the reason, soon it would not matter any more. For there would be John and the excitement of their reunion, and then their marriage and the settling in to a new home and a new life. Soon, so very soon, she would be with John again. She was glad that the journey was drawing to an end—very glad, she told herself. And she wondered why it seemed that she had to convince herself of the fact. Was it because a part of her, a small but treacherous and persistent part of her, had the insane wish that the journey would never end at all?

Trying to still the sudden trembling of her hands, she concentrated on the bush. They were driving slowly—Siane had seen the sign proclaiming a twenty-five mile per hour speed limit—and it was relatively simple to spot game when it was near the road. There were more impala. There were vultures wheeling in the air some distance away, and pheasants that wandered by the road only to scatter at the truck's approach. Once there was a giraffe, and André stopped the truck to let Siane get a better view of it. The gesture took her by surprise; nothing in his demeanour until now had indicated any kind of consideration for her. She turned and smiled her thanks. She did not expect an answering smile in return—that would be quite out of character for the rugged man with the arrogant manner—but nor did she expect a scrutiny which made her feel as helpless as she had been earlier that day when he had towelled her bare body dry. A confused sound came from parched lips, then she tore her gaze back to the giraffe.

Normally Siane would have been enchanted with the graciousness of the animal, the aloofness with which it nibbled at the high branches of a tree. But now there was no conscious pleasure in the sight.

There were only the hot tears pricking at her eye-lids and the desire—an insane desire which sprang from nowhere—to feel André's arms around her and his lips on hers.

She was glad when he started the car once more. There had been something altogether too poignant in the moments of stillness. The air had seemed to crackle with a tension so intense that it could al-most be felt. Was it possible that André could be unaware of that tension, she wondered despairingly, or was it something that existed only in her imagi-nation?

As the car covered the miles, Siane made a valiant effort to compose herself. Soon now they would arrive at the camp. John would be there, and he must guess nothing of her turmoil. It would upset him to know that his bride-to-be had let herself be-come so affected by another man that just his prox-imity left her dizzy. It would be doubly upsetting because the man was his friend, and friendship would be a precious thing in the isolation of the bushveld.

When she considered the matter rationally, there was no reason for John's friendship with André to be severed. She could not deny that the man at her side had the power to stir her, but this was only so in a physical sense. The journey had thrown them together to an extent she had never envisaged when she had stowed away beneath the canvas. It was only the enforced intimacy which had brought to the fore emotions and responses which she had never known she possessed.

But the journey was almost at an end. Once she was with John, glorying in the security of their love and their future together, the memory of the journey would fade, and her responses with it. Even if she were to meet André socially—the thought brought an involuntary quiver—she would be able to converse with him naturally. If they referred to the journey at all they would do so with humour. And that was all there was to it. There would be no painful memories, no dreams at night, because for that it was first necessary for Siane to have some affection for André—as always she shied away from the word 'love'—and she could hardly have affection for a man who was everything she detested.

Her thinking had logic, and that in itself was reassuring. There was no reason why it should also be painful.

The camp was in a clearing not far from the river. Years ago Siane had visited the Kruger Park, and vague memories of the holiday still lingered in her mind. John's descriptions of the camp at Crocodile View had been coloured with Siane's own re-collections of Skukuza and Satara, the camps at which she had stayed with her parents. Like tiny villages they had been, with great clusters of thatched huts, each camp with a store and a rest-aurant and a garage. Small outposts of civilisation in the middle of the bush. Somehow she had expected this camp to be similar.

With something like shock she looked around

her now at the place which was to be her home. It was very small, even smaller than she had imagined. There was one main structure, long and white-washed and attractive, with large picture windows for observing the animals when they came to the river to drink. This would be for the guests who came to the reserve. There was a view on to the river, on to the flat grey rocks where crocodiles lay for hours in the sun, as motionless as if they were dead. Now Siane understood the aptness of the reserve's name.

To one side was a smaller house, compact and with an air of spare efficiency—the administration block, she assumed. A little away was a thatched rondawel, with jasmine and golden shower cascading over the whitewashed walls. In a corner, nearer to the fence, was the last building, with the look of a dormitory about it; general staff quarters perhaps.

Coupled with the smallness of the camp was an air of extreme desolation. Siane had known the camp would be lonely, but this was a loneliness beyond anything she had anticipated. John had never led her to believe Crocodile View would be different. If she had had in her mind a modified version of the Kruger Park that was her own fault, Siane told herself firmly. And besides, what did it matter? She had come here to be with John because she loved him, because she could not envision a life without him. Any loneliness could only enhance

their togetherness and make it even more precious
than before.

She felt André's gaze upon her. She lifted her
head and saw the grey eyes studying her, steadily
and with a hint of the compassion she had noted
before. If he had sensed something of her shock she
must hasten to disillusion him.

'I take it that's John's?' she asked brightly, her
eyes going to the small thatched rondawel.

'Right.'

'Well then....' She hesitated just a moment. 'I'll
just take my belongings and put them down.'

She did not tell him that she was filled with a
sense of anti-climax. That somehow she had expected—foolishly as she realised now—that John
would come running to meet her with smiles and
exclamations of welcome. It was mid-morning and
the camp had an air of desertion. John would be
out somewhere, busy with his work.

She held out her hand. 'Thank you for bringing
me. I know John will be grateful too.'

But André did not take the proffered hand, and
after a moment she withdrew it. Feeling strangely
hurt, she looked up at him. He was still watching
her, but now the expression in his eyes had changed.
Her pulses quickened. If this man were anyone but
André she might take that look for approval, even
admiration. But the man *was* André, and admiration would be a feeling unknown to him. In any
event there could be neither approval nor admiration for a girl whom he regarded only with con-

tempt. Nevertheless, her pulses continued to beat faster than usual, and she had to drop her eyes lest he read her emotion.

'I'll just take my belongings,' she said again as matter-of-factly as she was able.

She had opened the door, and was about to go to the back of the truck when he stopped her. 'Let's find out where John is first.'

She wanted to tell him not to concern himself, that she could manage quite well on her own, but there was something so bleak about the isolated camp that she kept silent.

Together they walked to the rondawel with its golden tumble of flowering shrubs. The door was open, and André stepped aside to let her go in. It was ironic how things had worked out, she thought wryly as he followed her. Here was the moment she had dreamed of for so long—the crossing over the threshold into her new home. She had pictured it all so vividly—John's surprise, his joy. The drive to the nearest church to be married. Her parents had mentioned the question of banns, but she had refused to consider this a problem. The circumstances were so unusual that a clergyman would doubtless be prepared to marry them on the spot.

With the marriage licence in John's pocket they would have returned to Crocodile View, and John would have carried her, in love and with tenderness, across the threshold.

Yet now, when she should be in John's arms, a tall and virile stranger was with her instead, so close behind her that where her responses should be concentrated on taking in the details of her new home, she could feel only an aching awareness which was becoming all too familiar.

It was as if an invisible cord bound her to André, a cord that tingled and sparked with tension. She turned and looked at him. But there was nothing in his expression to indicate that he was in any way aware of the current that disturbed her so intensely.

Deliberately she willed herself to relax. Only then was she able to look around her. An open door revealed that there were two rooms. The rooms were clean, but filled with a clutter which reminded her so vividly of John that for the first time his unseen presence became real. Books lay open on a table, a safari suit hung over a chair. She saw the pipe he had loved to smoke, and on a wall was a print which had always been one of his favourites.

Dear John! She loved him so much. Two days spent in the company of an arrogant giant of a man had made all else seem to lose meaning. Now, standing in John's rondawel—and her own, she reminded herself—it came to Siane with a rush just how much she had missed him.

'You can leave me. I'll just wait here till John comes.' She spoke easily, and she was able to smile as she looked up at André.

An expression came and went in the grey eyes. 'When I'm satisfied,' was all he said.

He left her in the rondawel while he went to look around the camp. Without his disturbing presence Siane was able to make a closer inspection of her new home. The rooms were very small, and the furnishings were minimal. A bachelor pad. It was just right for a single man with undemanding tastes.

For the first time she wondered if she had been wrong to descend on John without warning. Perhaps he had planned to have a bigger house built before their marriage. Somehow she thought he might have had it in mind. Not that they could not be happy together in this place: they could. Fiercely almost, she clung to the knowledge. Now the rondawel was a bachelor pad, but when she had finished with it it would be a home. She would send for material to make curtains and cushions. There would be a colourful rug for the floor. A double bed would replace the small single one in the bedroom. How they would manage meanwhile was a thought she did not dwell on. They would be married, and they would manage.

What dismayed her more than the rondawel was the isolation and the loneliness of the camp. She should have known it would be like this, and yet in a sense she had not known. For the first time she wondered how she would occupy her days until the evenings when she and John could be together.

She was debating whether or not to unpack when footsteps sounded in the doorway, and she turned quickly, to find a tall figure watching her.

'You've found John?'

'I know where he is.'

'That's wonderful.' Siane was horrified at the lack of enthusiasm in her tone. 'Then it's goodbye, André.'

'No, spitfire.' Grey eyes studied her with a familiar hint of mockery. 'It seems I'm to be saddled with you a while longer.'

'What!' She stiffened.

'You're coming with me.'

She looked at him speechlessly for a moment, eyes wide and startled and very blue, her heart hammering painfully against her ribs. 'Something's happened to John?' she managed to whisper at last.

'No.' His voice was dry. 'He's away on a reconnaissance trip.'

'Oh....' Her lips were curiously dry, and a small pink tongue went out to moisten them. 'That's fine then. I'll just wait here till he comes.'

'He won't be back tonight. Come on, Siane, get moving.'

She looked at him uncertainly. 'You're taking me to a hotel?'

He was very tall, towering beside her like some ancient god of the forests. The line of his jaw was rigid and his body was taut with impatience. When she met his eyes she saw that he studied her with dispassionate intensity, as if he wondered that one stubborn girl could take up so much of his valuable time.

'A hotel?' The question was sardonic. 'I'm taking you to my farm.'

'No!' She sprang away from him. 'I won't come!'

'You will.' His tone was authoritative. It came to Siane that André Connors was not accustomed to being disobeyed. Perversely the realisation brought out the rebel in her.

'You can't force me,' she threw at him.

'Can't I?'

The voice was soft, but the hands that shot out to grasp her arms were merciless in their strength. Easily he pulled her to him, so close that she could feel the length of his body burning her through the thin fabric of her clothes. The sensual smell of maleness was all around her, filling her nostrils with a potency that sent her senses reeling so that she found it difficult to think.

'You will do as I say.' A soft voice, infinitely dangerous.

'No!' Helplessly she tried to twist away from him. 'It wouldn't be right.'

His laughter was low and sensuous as it fanned her hot cheek. Like a cat playing with a mouse he held her from him and looked down into a small flushed face, taking in the eyes that were wide and blue and eloquent with pleading, the lips that trembled, the pulse that throbbed in the hollow of a slender throat.

'You're a strange mixture, spitfire,' he said softly. 'You think nothing of stowing away with a stranger. But after hours of intimacy'—she flinched at the emphasis he gave the last word—'you withdraw like an outraged maiden at the thought of spending a night in his house.'

'You make everything sound so ugly. You're the meanest person I ever met!' Her voice was low-toned and filled with hatred.

'And you're certainly the most foolish.' His own tone was equable, but she saw a muscle tighten in his jaw.

'I suppose I have been foolish,' she conceded. No purpose in arguing that particular point. She had been thinking along the same lines for some time now. 'But I don't need to make matters any worse.'

'Correct,' he agreed crisply. 'That's precisely why you will take your possessions and stop wasting my time.'

'I'm staying here.' She lifted her head mutinously.

'I will give you exactly one minute.'

The statement had a dangerous ring. What would he do if she defied him? Siane wondered. Excitement stirred in her, but the eyes that met his were without expression. 'You can't force me!' she said, more uncertainly this time.

'You are throwing down the gauntlet, aren't you?' His eyes moved over her with a familiarity that was a deliberate insult. 'And you want me to take up the challenge.' As his arms pulled her defiant body easily to him, she heard a mocking, 'I wonder if John has any idea of what he's letting himself in for.'

Later she was to wonder if there was a moment in which she could have escaped from an embrace which owed nothing to affection, and was only a demonstration of mastery. But that would only come later.... For as the muscled arms tightened about her slender body, moulding the soft feminine curves to a hard male angularity, there was only a wild rushing of sensation which amounted to ecstasy. His lips crushed hers with a demanding remorselessness, forcing her mouth open so that she could feel his teeth against hers. Time had no meaning now; there was only the world of the senses, a flaming current through the veins and the nerve-stream. A mad desire, an utterly crazy desire that this moment need never end.

When he put her from him she could only gaze at him through a blur. She felt drained and at the same time vibrantly alive. The face that looked down at her was a bleak mask. There was a whitening around the nostrils, and she could hear that his breathing had quickened. But the eyes were without expression, and his tone, when he spoke, was as hard as ever.

'With that settled, perhaps we can get moving.'

The derision in his tone was like the blade of a knife. Anger flared in Siane, hot and searing. How dared he treat her like this! As if she were no more than a helpless puppy whom he could tease and manipulate as it suited his pleasure. He had the power to excite her, a physical appeal that was more devastating than anything she had ever encountered before. And he was using it to crush her, to punish her for stowing away when he did not want her, and for daring to join a man to whom, in his elevated opinion, she was unsuited. Well, she would show him!

'No!' Now her own voice was as derisive as his. 'I will not come. Your petty little display hasn't changed my mind in the least.'

'So it's brute force you want.' His eyes glittered as he took a step towards her once more. 'My God, spitfire, I wonder if you know quite what you're doing.'

Her attempts at resistance were a mere token. His strength was far greater than hers, and as he dragged her out of the rondawel there was nothing she could do to free herself. There was nothing gentle in the hands that dumped her in the truck, then threw her luggage in after her. When he got in at the driver's side she kept her head turned away from him, so that he would not see the tears that made a hot path down her cheeks. Not tears of hurt or self-pity, but of rage. Rage at him for his brutal unfeelingness, an even greater rage at herself at the knowledge that even while she had hated him for his treatment, she had yet gloried in his strength. Something had happened to her in the last two days, something she did not understand in the least, and for which she despised herself, and yet it was something she seemed quite powerless to resist.

'Where are you taking me?' she asked at length, when the tears had been blinked away and she had regained some measure of control.

'I told you—my place.' His tone was terse.

'What will John say?'

'Are you asking me whether he'll challenge me to a duel because I've carried you off to my lair?' She flinched at his tone. 'Hardly, my dear spitfire. He'll be glad that I did the only thing possible in the circumstances.'

'Why ... why didn't you just let me stay at Crocodile View?' she whispered unhappily.

'Because, spitfire, even I couldn't allow a foolish child to remain by herself in a lonely camp in the midst of a game park.'

'I would have been all right.' It was an effort to speak positively, when, for no reason that she could explain, his words threatened to bring new tears.

'You're familiar with the conditions?' Again the hardness.

She shook her head. 'But I'd have managed. I'll have to learn sooner or later.' And then, when he did not speak, 'There must have been someone around....'

'Not a soul.'

She turned, caught by an anger in his tone which she did not understand. 'Guests ... rangers....'

'Nobody. Crocodile View is run more for the pleasure of its owner than for the small profit guests might bring.'

'But I thought....' She was puzzled. 'John said people come to see game.'

'They do. But not all that often. This isn't the Kruger Park, Siane.'

'I know.' She was breathless. Strange how his use of her real name could affect her. 'But the rangers.

Where were they?'

'With John.'

So he really had acted out of concern for her, this strange disturbing man, with the arrogant exterior and the manner that could mingle an occasional tenderness with a ruthless savageness.

'Then you were thinking of me....'

'You?' A harsh laugh. 'Anything that might happen to you is only what you've asked for. No, spitfire, I was thinking of John.'

'You wouldn't care if I was eaten by a lion!' she tossed at him furiously.

Grey eyes skimmed her with a dispassionate hardness. 'John would care.'

And that seemed to take care of that question.

CHAPTER SEVEN

SIANE could have retaliated with a biting retort of her own, but she restrained herself. In any interchange with André Connors she seemed to be the inevitable loser. His last comment was so outrageous that nothing she could have said would have answered it adequately. Far better to treat the comment with the silent contempt it deserved. For the moment she was at the mercy of this rugged man of the bush, who, it seemed, had never been near enough to civilisation to have learned any manners. To pit herself against him would be as futile as to force a sapling to fight a strong wind. She could only hope that John would return soon, then she could forget the nightmare of this trip, and adjust to her new life in peace.

For a while they drove on in silence. Siane had no heart left for more sparring, and small-talk would have been impossible. André offered no comments on the distance to be travelled, and Siane did not ask. She had no option but to go where he took her. For the moment she was in his hands—figuratively speaking only, she reminded herself fiercely, for on no account would she allow him to make love to her ever again. No matter if her treacherous body clamoured for him to possess her.

She kept her eyes on the scenery beyond her window. Even through her misery she could understand the magic that drew John to this place. There was a grandeur about the bushveld. Not a picture-postcard kind of beauty, but an untamed wildness that haunted the mind and enlivened the imagination. Everything had its place here—the thorny trees and the long veld grass, the scrub-covered kopjies, standing eternal watch over the countryside. The herds of impala grazing in sheltered clearings, graceful bodies poised and alert for flight in a world where danger was ever-present. The giraffes that stood tall and aloof beside the highest trees, and the herds of wildebeest and zebras, amicable companions. The birds, in colours more vivid than those of the Highveld, and in the cloudless sky the vultures, wheeling, soaring, ceaselessly on the look-out for carrion. And somewhere in the long grass would be the lions, hidden and sleepy perhaps in the heat of the sun, but ready for the kill when their bellies rumbled.

This was Africa in the raw, the bushveld as it had been for centuries before the coming of civilisation. Here there was room only for the strong, and the name of the game was survival. She would be one of the strong ones, Siane vowed. She would prove André wrong. And she wondered why it should matter.

They had taken a different route from the one they had previously travelled, and the gate by which they left the park was not the one through which

they had entered. As they came to the national road,
it was like stepping back into another world. They
were back in a land where fields were cultivated and
where men took from the soil what they could.

They came to timber country once more. The
road rose and dipped against the contours of the
hills, and again there was a never-ending vista of
incredible views. They could no longer be far from
wherever André was taking her.

André made no comment when he turned off the
highway and drove the short distance to a pair of
great wrought iron gates bearing the name 'Pinelands'. He stopped the truck and Siane watched him
go to the gates and swing them open. She did not
need to ask whether he was the owner of what was
obviously a timber plantation. It was evident in
every inch of his bearing. It was there in the confident manner, in the lithe sureness of his gait. And
it was there in the moment when he stopped and
looked for a moment across a forested slope, like a
man who had been away from the place he loved
and was taking it all in again. For no reason at all
Siane felt a lump form in the back of her throat.

He came back to the truck, drove through the
gates, then closed them again before driving further.
Even now he did not speak, and pride stilled the
questions she longed to ask.

But pride did not keep her from looking at the
forests as they drove on. Everywhere there were
signs of activity. Bundles of logs, a lorry piled high
with timber, a group of wood-cutters sipping tea

in the shade of the trees. André did not stop the
truck, but Siane noticed that wherever there were
men, good feeling and respect were revealed in the
raising of battered hats, in hands lifted in greeting,
in smiles. Clearly André was a man who knew how
to combine efficiency with fairness. As she had
imagined, his workers seemed to enjoy being under
his command. And again there came the wondering
whether a woman would enjoy it likewise. Not Siane
herself, for she would never be in the position of
having to take orders from him. She would have
John, and she knew what their relationship would
be—easy and peaceful and contented, as it had been
since they were children. But for a woman who decided to make her life with André, who loved him
and was loved by him in return, what would her
life be? Siane tried to quell the tiny knife of pain
at the knowledge that this was one question to which
she would never know the answer.

She caught her breath as they rounded a bend
and the homestead appeared quite suddenly in
sight. Dimly she was aware that André had turned
his head, and that his eyes were on her. Important
though it seemed not to let him guess at her feelings,
it was impossible to keep the awe from her face. The
house rose large and white and graceful against the
forested slope of a mountain. The roof had a single
gable, curved and perfect and much like the gables
Siane had seen in the winelands of the Cape. Falling
away from the house was a garden, lush and tropical
with bougainvillea and hibiscus and the delicate

blooms of the frangipani blending together in a lovely riot of colour.

This was where André Connors lived? She had thought his home would be like himself, spare and rugged and basic. He had slowed the truck and in his eyes was a look of quiet satisfaction. And it came to Siane that she had been wrong in her assessement. This lovely home was his real setting.

At that moment she forgot her resolve to keep silent. 'It's beautiful,' she said simply.

'I'm glad you like it, Siane.'

For once the grey eyes held neither mockery nor derision. Instead there was a warmth in them which Siane had never expected. In this man, with his toughness and his ruthlessness, the warmth seemed a rare and very wonderful thing. As in the moments when she had seen him look over his lands, she felt the inexplicable lump at the back of her throat.

The magic of the moment did not last more than a few seconds. Then André was driving once more, leaving the forestry road to sweep up the drive that ran in a curve before the house.

Servants seemed to appear as if from nowhere, and again Siane noted the affection and respect she had glimpsed in the forests. André was back after an absence, and they were glad.

Maria, the housekeeper, showed her to her room. Siane was relieved that there were other people in the house. And then, as she followed the woman down a long passage, it came to her that in one sense the thought was as irrational as André had made it out to be. She had stowed away in the vehicle of a stranger without a thought for appearances or decorum. She had spent a night with him on a truck-seat no more than five feet wide. She had emerged naked from a pool and submitted while he wrapped a towel about her shivering body. And now she was worrying about whether or not she would be adequately chaperoned in the man's house which was so large that it seemed to have no less than five bedrooms. André was not the only one who would say that she had come very late to her senses.

She herself could see the irony of the situation, yet it was true that the mere presence of servants in the house gave her an odd sense of security. Could it be, she wondered with a small stab of dismay, that the reason lay in the fact that she could no longer rely on her senses or her body not to betray her?

There was little opportunity to ponder the flash of self-knowledge which was as preposterous as it was unwelcome. Lunch would be served in half an hour, Maria told her as she opened a door and waited for Siane to precede her into the room.

There was just time to bath and to change out of clothes which were grubby from the long journey. A bathroom led from the bedroom. Siane ran the water, then went back into the room. She looked about her liking what she saw. The room was not big, but it had an air of light and space. Curtains and carpet and bedspread were in shades of blue and green, cool colours that would make the room seem inviting on even the hottest bushveld day. So far Siane had seen very little of the house, yet enough to know that it had been furnished not only with expense but also with innate good taste. She wondered who had chosen the colours which mingled and blended and seemed to extend into the garden outside the windows, and the furniture, all light-coloured and shaped in long low elegant lines.

While the water was running, she went to the window and looked out over the garden. Was André married? She had never asked him the question. The probability of the answer filled her with a dull sort of pain.

Surely, she mused, as she lay back in the bath some minutes later, if there was a mistress at Pinelands she would have been at the door to welcome her husband. Of course, André's wife would not have known when he would be back. She could be riding somewhere through the forests. Or she could have driven to the nearest village to do shopping.

Unbidden there came the thought that in the same situation she herself would have remained at the homestead waiting for him, no matter that she did not know when he would come.

Enough! Getting out of the bath, she began to dry herself with rough, angry movements. Her mind was getting the better of her: it was becoming as unpredictable as her body. How André and his wife would laugh if they knew the drift of her thoughts. Perhaps they were laughing even now, indulgently amused at the tale of the impatient bride who had stowed away in the back of a stranger's truck with her wedding-dress.

When she was dry she went back into the room and looked thoughtfully through her suitcase. A few minutes ago all that had mattered was to get out of her travel-weary clothes and feel refreshed in something clean. Now it was equally important that she look presentable. And pretty, whispered a voice inside her, but she pushed it away. Well might the Connors laugh at her, but they should also respect her. She would not have John disgraced because it was said that his bride was not good enough for him.

It took her a while to make a decision, but then she dressed quickly. She took a look in the mirror before leaving the room. It was not often that Siane took the trouble to study her appearance. This time she did. Dark curls, tidy for once, framed a small oval face that was piquant and young and somehow vulnerable. Cheeks were soft and a little flushed, and the eyes were wide and luminous and very blue. A soft cheesecloth blouse moulded an intensely feminine figure, showing to advantage a long slim neck and smooth honey-coloured arms. A blue skirt hung in graceful pleats from a trim belted waist, and thonged sandals were on bare feet.

Her heart lifted. Even now she might not be considered a suitable wife for John. But there was satisfaction, however slight, in the knowledge that the arrogant André Connors would be seeing her, just this once, at her best.

Vaguely she remembered the direction of the

dining-room. It was empty, but the table, she saw at a glance, was laid for three. Voices came to her from beyond the window, then there was the sound of André's laugh, low and vibrant and very amused. French doors led from the room. Siane took a deep breath—as if braving herself for some dreadful ordeal, she thought wryly—then she stepped through the doors on to a wide paved patio.

The conversation came to a sudden halt as she appeared. Two faces looked up at her. André, and the woman with whom he was sitting. Dimly Siane was aware that he gestured to a chair, that they were waiting for her to sit, but only dimly, for her heart was beating uncomfortably fast and her knees had gone suddenly weak.

She had known he would be married, so there was no reason for her to feel quite so shocked. Was it just that the mental image of André's wife had been so different from the reality? Had she in fact even had a mental image? Or was it that the cool and sophisticated beauty of the woman who was making no attempt to hide her curiosity made her feel a vulnerability which the change of clothes did nothing to lessen? Yet even that did not fully explain her shock.

True understanding would come only later, in the stillness of her room, when she would realise that there was a part of her which had never accepted that André could be married, and perhaps never would.

'The little stowaway.' The voice was as cool as the

eyes that studied her. 'How very unconventional!'

And childishly absurd, the tone seemed to imply. As Siane made an effort to sit down gracefully—no easy feat when her limbs moved with a treacherous weakness—she thought crossly that the other woman would never resort to a similar mode of transport no matter the circumstances. Which explained, perhaps, André's own attitude to the escapade.

'Unconventional? Purely in the eye of the beholder,' Siane murmured, and saw the glitter in André's eyes. Was he amused? Or was he angry that she had dared to provoke his wife? Too late it came to her that she was beholden to this woman for her hospitality. Contrite now, she said with more warmth, 'I appreciate your letting me stay here, Mrs Connors.'

'I'm not Mrs Connors.'

An uncontrollable leaping of the heart. Involuntarily Siane's head jerked up, but she managed to lower long-lashed lids so that the wild joy would not be seen in her eyes.

'André darling,' the husky voice was brittle and amused, 'you've neglected to make the introductions.'

The irrational joy was shortlived. There was no mistaking the familiarity in the endearment. 'I'm not Mrs Connors,' the woman had said. Her tone implied the words 'Not yet....'

Barbara Sinclair.... Siane O'Brien.... André made the introductions smoothly. She was asked what she would drink. André had a beer and Barbara a sherry. Siane asked for lemonade. And let them make of that what they liked, she thought defiantly. Already they thought her a child, a foolish tomboy. Her simple taste in beverages could hardly make their opinion of her any lower than it was already.

She was glad when the drink was put in front of her, and she could nurse the glass in her hands. It gave her something to do, and she was able to keep her eyes down, hiding the confusion which churned inside her. The conversation continued where, evidently, it had left off when she had apppeared on the patio. Barbara directed the flow of the talk, Siane noticed, and no attempt was made to include her. Even if she had wanted to speak, there was nothing she could have contributed. The talk was all of places and people she did not know, and through it ran a strain of intimacy and long familiarity. Barbara was amusing in a quick malicious manner, and André's laughter indicated his appreciation.

'Will you be here long?' Barbara asked, when they were seated at the dining-room table, and the lunch was put before them.

Siane looked up quickly, caught by the hostility, just barely disguised, in the husky voice. Had André not mentioned the reason for her coming?

'Oh, no, I'm getting married to John Lang. I thought you knew....' Her words trailed away as she saw the meaning look Barbara darted at André. Something made her add stiffly, 'I'm waiting for him now.'

'But how very exciting!' For the first time there was friendliness in the other woman's tone. 'Darling, can't you just see your little stowaway as the perfect wife for a game ranger?'

Siane braced herself to withstand one of André's mocking comments. Strangely there was just a tightening of the lips before he said, very smoothly, 'A glass of wine with your veal, Barbara?'

Barbara Sinclair left soon after the meal, with an invitation to André to dine at her home a few days later. Siane watched her drive away, a svelte figure in a sleek red sports car which seemed oddly out of place in the ruggedness of the bushveld. When the car was no more than a red dust-speck at the end of the drive, Siane turned to André. His face was set and grim. He was once more the autocrat Siane had come to know so well. Silence had fallen with Barbara's departure, and Siane was at a loss to know what to do or say next.

'I think I'll take a walk around the garden,' she said tentatively.

'Do you ride?' The question was abrupt.

She looked up quickly. 'Yes.'

'I'm off to the saw-mills. If you'd like to join me, Maria will get you some breeches....'

His tone was so curt, so forbidding, that she hesitated.

'Well?' he barked impatiently.

This time she did not hesitate. He need not have invited her if he did not want to. She smiled up at him. 'I'd like that.'

She was unaware that her eyes were very blue, wide and sparkling beneath long dark lashes. She saw only the hardening in his own eyes, and once again the forbidding tightening of the lips. She caught her breath, the smile dying. But she did not change her mind, for there was a compulsion within her to know more of the life he led before she left Pinelands.

The breeches fitted her well. Whoever they belonged to was the same size as Siane, with just the waist a little bigger. Barbara? she wondered. And if her riding clothes were at Pinelands, what other clothes did she leave here? The thought of the woman's possessions in one of the bedrooms, probably André's, was painful.

Abruptly, angry at her own morbid preoccupation, Siane slapped a brush through tumbled curls. When she ran outside André was waiting for her.

A mare had been saddled for her, a lovely animal with gentle eyes and the sleek body of a racehorse. André helped her to mount. Siane could have managed quite easily by herself, but the hands that lifted her made her feel so protected and feminine, a creature so at variance with the tomboy stowaway who had hidden beneath the canvas in the back of a truck that she did nothing to stop him. There was little she could have done anyway, for the strong touch on her waist had set her heart racing in a way that was alarming.

André's own horse was a gelding, tall and powerful as its owner, with glossy black flanks and muscles which rippled like smoothly oiled mechanisms when it moved. Together, horse and rider, they made a stunning picture of sheer maleness.

Barbara was forgotten as they left the stableyard and cantered along a track which led to the forests, the gelding leading, the mare, high-spirited yet gentle with it, content to follow. They reached the forests, and the horses slowed to a trot, for the path was narrow now, and there was an occasional branch overhead. It was cool beneath the trees, a pleasant respite from the burning bushveld heat. The air was fresh, spicy with the mingled aromas of pine and spruce and eucalyptus. Siane was exhilarated, and filled with a happiness she had not known in a long while.

André was just slightly ahead, and she saw how he turned his head now to this side, now to that, inspecting, noting, remembering. His sureness and alertness gave her an odd warming pleasure. There was something peculiarly exciting in observing the man moving through his own particular domain.

At the saw-mills they dismounted. While André spoke to the foreman, Siane looked about her with interest. The place was a hub of activity. There was the shrieking of electric saws, and the dull thud of logs being loaded on to a truck. The ground was soft with shavings, and the air was sweet with the scent of resin. There was an atmosphere of efficiency and good order, yet unlike an industry in the city, there was also a sense of serenity.

When André had finished his conversation he

beckoned to her, and she followed him through the mill. Siane was impressed as he began to explain the nature of the mill's operations. She had not known how much was involved between the time of felling the trees to the point where the timber was ready to be used. Now and then, when André's eyes were on some piece of machinery, or when he ran a hand along a fine-grained piece of wood, Siane was able to look at him unobserved. She was seeing a new André; not the man who had lashed at her with his tongue, or who had stirred her blood with his touch, but a man who loved his work, who was totally dedicated to his career, who took pride in every inch of the land and the forests and the machinery that were his.

They stayed a while longer at the mill, and as André concentrated once more on his work, Siane was content to stay in the background and take in the scene all around her. Presently he came back to her and said it was time to go back.

They were quiet as they rode along the forest trails. For once there was no strain in the quietness, rather it seemed that they both were occupied with their own thoughts. Siane was thinking of all she had seen in the last two days—Wilgespruit, the camping place by the stream, Pinelands, Crocodile View. A pang of guilt shot through her at the thought of the game park, and at the knowledge that she had not thought of John for several hours.

Unhappily she stared at the strong back of the man on the gelding. How different things would have been if she had arrived at Wilgespruit on the day the bus was due to go, for then she never would have thought of stowing away in a stranger's truck.

Basically, of course, nothing had changed. She would still be married to John, and together they would cement a relationship which seemed to have existed always. John would never know of the turmoil and the confusion which had raged in her for the two eventful days of her journey. She would see to that. But as far as she herself was concerned, Siane knew that life would never be quite the same again.

CHAPTER EIGHT

THEY emerged from the forests to find shadows across the veld. The long warm afternoon was drawing to a close. The horses were eager to get back; Siane could feel the spirited movement of the mare beneath her, could see the gelding's impatient flexing of muscles. André let the horse have his head, and as he cantered away Siane followed swiftly on the mare. She did not know that she laughed out loud, a sound that was thrown forward by the wind to the man in front of her. She knew only the joy of speed, of the moving mare, of the wind that tossed her hair.

They reached the stable-yard. When André had dismounted he reached up to help Siane to the ground. She let him lift her down, then laughed up at him. 'Thank you,' she said warmly, 'that was just lovely.'

'I'm glad.' The words were said simply, but his hands were still on her waist, and there was an expression in his eyes which made her suddenly breathless. She had the feeling that he was about to say something more when the sound of a horse's hooves made them turn.

André's hands left her waist abruptly, and Siane shaded her eyes as a big grey horse rode in to the yard across the path of the setting sun, and a young girl slid quickly and gracefully to the ground.

'Well, Lindy.' André was smiling as he greeted her.

'Hello, André.' A dimple came and went as she grinned back at him. 'I heard you were back.'

'News travels fast.'

'Especially when it comes via Barbara Sinclair!' The girl grimaced impishly, in a manner which endeared her instantly to Siane. 'Dad asked me to ride over with the report on the horses.'

'Could have waited till tomorrow,' André said good-humouredly, and in a way which indicated that his relationship with this girl was purely platonic. 'Thanks anyway.' He turned. 'Lindy, meet Siane.'

'Hello, Siane.' Another smile, friendly and unaffected, reinforcing Siane's feeling that she could like this girl. Her spirits lifted. It was reassuring to know that a girl of her own age lived nearby. Barbara Sinclair she had already discounted—she and Barbara would never have anything in common. But Lindy, with her dimpled cheeks and open freckled smile, would be a friend.

'Come up to the house,' André invited. 'Maria will have some coffee waiting.'

'I'd like that.' And then, turning to Siane, she said with lively curiosity, 'Barbara said something about a stowaway. She couldn't have meant you!'

'I'm afraid she did.' Siane made a rueful mouth.

'Really!' The freckled face lit up with excitement. 'How fantastic!'

'It had its moments,' came the reluctant admission. Involuntarily Siane glanced at André. He was watching her. There was a curving at the corners of his mouth, and his eyes held an expression which she could not define. Mockery? Amusement? No, not quite. Rather a combination of the two mixed with something else. Siane's heart hammered painfully. Was he remembering the moments by the stream, when he had wrapped the towel around her bare wet body before drying it with movements that could have been deliberately sensual? Or was it the memory of the way he had kissed her at Crocodile View before dragging her to his truck which had brought the unnerving gleam to the dark eyes?

'You've come to stay?' Lindy was saying. 'Oh, I hope so. We could be friends.'

'We will be,' said Siane, trying to take a grip on her emotions. She lifted her chin and forced a smile. 'Of course I won't be living at Pinelands.'

'Oh?'

'I'll be at Crocodile View. I'm going to be married to John Lang.'

A queer little hush greeted the remark. Somewhere at the back of her mind Siane registered that the light had died in Lindy's eyes, but she was still too dazed herself to attach any meaning thereto.

'Shall we go up to the house now?' André's words intruded into the silence.

'Thanks, André, but no.' The other girl sounded strained. 'I ... I wasn't thinking just now when I said. . . .' She hesitated. 'Well, it's really rather late.'

'As you wish, Lindy.' Siane had never heard André so gentle. 'Say thanks to your father for the notes.'

'I like her,' Siane said when Lindy had ridden away and she and André were walking back through the garden. Actually her mind was not so much on the other girl as on the need to make conversation. She was too acutely aware of the man at her side. The aura of compelling maleness which he exuded in such measure was so heady that, despite all her efforts, the turbulence of her emotions would not be stilled. Only small talk could lessen the tension which tingled like an electric current in the air between them. 'I really do hope we'll be friends.'

The low chuckle was so sensuous as to unnerve her. She looked at him uncertainly. It was still light enough to see the derision in his eyes as he studied her. Deliberately his gaze lingered on the lips which had responded beneath his, then descended to the soft feminine curves which were evident even in the riding attire.

'André!' She tried to suppress the quiver in her tone. 'Why ... why are you laughing?'

'You really don't know?' A hand reached for her chin, cupping it with long lean fingers, tilting her face so that she had to look up at him. There was amusement in his voice, but it was an amusement which did not reach his eyes. 'You have the body of a woman, and yet in some ways you are even more of a child than I thought, little Siane.'

Little Siane.... Spoken by somebody else there could have been tenderness in the use of her name. But there was no tenderness in this man, with the look of granite and steel and the devilish features which were becoming more and more attractive in Siane's eyes.

'I suppose you're comparing me with Barbara,' she ground out.

Another chuckle. 'Hardly, spitfire. There's no similarity between you and Barbara except for the obvious'—again his eyes deliberately raked her slender form—'so there's little point in a comparison.'

Wrenching away from the hand that held her, Siane dropped her eyes and walked blindly further. It seemed there was no limit to André's sarcasm and desire to wound. He would be getting no more than he deserved when he married Barbara Sinclair. Arrogance and ruthlessness on his side, icy beauty and unfeeling sophistication on hers—what a match they would make! Both parties would find in their union the things they desired. André would have a wife whose poise and worldliness would make her the perfect hostess when there were people to be entertained at Pinelands. Barbara would have the satisfaction of being the wife of a wealthy man, mistress of a big and very lovely estate. It would not matter to them that they would never know the joy of sharing and loving and togetherness, the qualities which would be the essential components of Siane's marriage with John.

Let them have joy of each other, she thought fiercely—and wished that the picture of Barbara Sinclair as André's wife—as the woman he would care for most in the world—did not give her such pain.

Dinner was a silent meal. The meal was simple but delicious, yet Siane had to force herself not to play with her food. André would assume that the fresh air and the ride through the forests had made her hungry. Reluctance on her part to eat would provoke further mockery, and she had had more than enough of that.

When they had finished eating André said he had papers to go through and phone calls to make, and Siane said she could amuse herself. Actually she was relieved when he went from the room and she could drop her mask of bright unconcern.

She would go to her room, she thought. She did not want to remain in the living-room where she would see André when he emerged from his study. In fact, though that would be difficult to achieve, she would rather not see him again at all. There was no way she could prevent any social contact with André. André *and* Barbara, she corrected herself. But if she could limit that contact until after she was married, it might become easier to endure.

If only John would come for her tomorrow! She could not wait to leave Pinelands.

As she looked about the pretty bedroom, she felt strangely claustrophobic. It was too early to go to bed—she had never in her life felt less tired. Nor did she want to sit and read. Taking a cardigan from her suitcase she put it over her shoulders and left the room. It was very quiet in the house. Light showed beneath the closed door of the room which she took to be André's study. She paused as she came to it, then walked quickly past it, to slip through a side door she had spotted earlier in the day.

Some of the sun's heat still lingered in the bush-veld night, making the evening just warm enough to be pleasant. The African sky was a blaze of stars, their radiance silvering the garden and giving enough light for Siane to see by. The tropical air was fragrant with the mingled scents of exotic shrubs—the sweetness of the frangipani, and the headiness of gardenias and jasmine and honey-suckle. In other circumstances, Siane thought, she would enjoy this. Now, however, her body ached with a nameless yearning, and her mind was a turmoil of thoughts and emotions which made little sense.

And yet make sense of them she must. Tomorrow or the next day John would be here to claim her. By the end of the week she would be married. The day for which she had been waiting so long was almost upon her. Yet now that she was to be a bride she felt that she had never been less ready for it.

Did she love John? The question was rhetorical. She had loved John for so many years that she could not remember a time when she had not loved him. Even to question her feelings seemed disloyal. For John loved her too, and if he had any inkling of the doubts that assailed her now, he would be deeply wounded. He would not understand that she could love a man so much that she felt a part of him, and yet be stirred by another man to the point where she could no longer trust herself when she was with him.

From the first André had made her feel vibrant and excited and deliciously alive. He had invoked in her feelings and responses which she had never before experienced. Now, in the dark, she could admit that much to herself. André Connors had a virile masculinity which called forth from her a response which was primitive and basic and essentially female. Regret it she did, but the regret was in her mind, while the feelings that came to her when she was with André applied purely to the senses.

Somehow she would have to try to keep out of his way until she could leave Pinelands. Any further exposure to his devastating physical appeal could only deepen the sense of loss when the time came for parting.

That parting would have had to come even if John were not in the picture. For there was Barbara. She remembered the coy implication in Barbara's voice when she had said she was not Mrs Connors, the expression in her eyes when she had looked at André. Into her mind came a picture of the woman, a little older than Siane, and with a flawless and exotic beauty which Siane could not hope to match. Even assuming Siane had wished to compete with her for André's favours, it was a competition which she could not fail to lose, she thought wryly.

Unbidden there came into her mind yet another picture. Lindy.... The smile leaving the pretty freckled face, and the light dying in her eyes. Perhaps it was a measure of Siane's own turmoil that she had failed to understand the implications of that look until now. Was Lindy in love with John? If so, here was a further complication, and one which she did not know how to handle.

She wondered if John was aware of Lindy's feelings. Probably he was not, just as André would never know how Siane felt about him. What a tangled web, she reflected sadly. Or was this just the way of life? One could love and not be loved in return. One could suffer and all the while the object of the agony might be totally unaware of anything amiss.

She had taken an instant liking to Lindy, and would have liked to spare the other girl any hurt. But there was little she could do. Lindy would resent any efforts on Siane's part to explain or apologise. Like Siane herself, Lindy would have to find her own way of dealing with her problem.

A slight breeze stirred, deepening the tropical fragrances and the night insects sang shrilly. Such a short time since she had left her home, Siane mused. She had imagined that she would be exchanging the hectic bustle of city life for the calm serenity of the bushveld. Little had she dreamed that there would be a set of complications which would bring at least two people unhappiness.

She walked a little way along a paved path, turning back when she came to the shadowed blackness of the trees. She was approaching a low stone wall when she saw the tiny red spark of a lighted cigarette, and abruptly she stopped. She was about to walk the other way when André's voice came to her through the darkness.

'Going somewhere?'

'Back to the house.' The words emerged jerkily. He was nearer than she had thought.

'Because of me?'

'Of course not!' The denial was too emphatic.

'I frighten you.' It was a statement, not a question. Siane heard the familiar mocking note in his tone.

Damn the man! He was far too perceptive. And then a new thought came, an unwelcome one. If he knew she was frightened, perhaps he knew too that her heart was pounding far too rapidly against her ribs.

'You like to flatter yourself,' she said, trying to sound matter-of-fact.

'Do I?' he drawled. 'Come here, spitfire.'

'No.'

'Yes.' A hand took her arm and detained her too easily. 'Were you never taught to be polite to your host?'

'You're not my host,' she choked. And then, 'Well, yes, you are, but not because you want it this way.'

'And what do you know of my wants?' His voice was sleek and soft, with an extra quality which sent the blood rushing to Siane's cheeks.

'You made your feelings clear from the start.' She was glad that she could speak normally. Thank heavens it was so dark! Even André could not see well enough in the dark to register the heat that stained her cheeks or the pulse that throbbed in the hollow of her throat. 'Will John be here tomorrow?'

'Perhaps.' He was noncommittal. 'You're in a hurry to see him?'

'Well, of course. What an extraordinary question! I mean, I want to marry him, and I've come all this way to be with him.' The words tumbled out, but somehow she could not stop. 'I can't wait to see him.'

A chuckle, so derisive that she stiffened. 'What a long speech when a simple yes would have been answer enough.' He paused, and unbelievably, outrageously, a hand slid beneath her hair. 'You do know what it means to protest too much?'

'No ... yes. ...' It was hard to think when the long fingers encircled her throat. One finger rested lightly on the wild throb of pulse. 'I ... I'm not protesting.'

'We won't argue the point.' He was so close to her now that when he spoke she could feel the warmth of his breath caress her cheek. A weakness attacked her limbs, and she was aware of nothing but the desire to feel him touch her. Mentally she was readying herself for his kiss, when he said, 'Tell me about John.'

There was a lump in her throat that made it difficult to speak. 'You ... you know John,' she managed to whisper.

'I know a game-ranger.' His voice was dry, at variance with the sensuousness of the finger which began to stroke her throat in a movement which was slow and tantalising. 'I want to know about the man who can get a girl to embark on a trip like yours just so that she can be near him.'

'We ... we're engaged,' she whispered. 'You know that.'

'I asked you about John.' The questioning was relentless.

'He's strong and good and kind and handsome and....' Her words trailed away for a moment. Then she said, 'He's everything that you are not, André Connors.'

She thought his body stiffened. But then she heard him laugh, the sound short and dry, and she knew she had been mistaken. 'And you've been in love with him for how long?'

'Ever since I was a little girl.' She felt his mockery rather than saw it. 'I don't expect you to understand, André. But John was my friend, my companion, my brother. And now he's going to be my husband.'

'One doesn't marry a brother, spitfire.' There was danger in the voice that fanned her cheek.

'He's not my real brother,' she said defensively.

'Has it ever occurred to you that you know your John rather too well?' Still that deadly softness.

'I don't know what you're trying to imply,' she

countered hotly. 'I love John—I've always loved him. And he loves me.'

'Spoken with such certainty. You're so sure of yourself, Siane.' He paused. 'Are you as sure of John?'

Something in his tone sent an unexpected flicker of uneasiness running down her spine. It was stupid to let him get at her like this! By now she should know that André delighted in riling her. And yet the uneasiness persisted. 'Absolutely sure,' she tossed at him.

'It's a year since you saw him last?'

She wanted to wrench away from him, tell him that his questions were insulting and none of his business. But she could not stir while his fingers tantalised her with their sensual movements.

'You know that....'

'Things could have changed since then.' The suggestion was made lightly, but Siane caught the meaning behind it.

'You're thinking of Lindy,' she said with sudden understanding. 'I saw ... this afternoon....'

'Well?'

'Lindy will get over it. She'll meet someone else.' There was a hint of despair in her tone as she went on. 'It happens. One falls in love and ... and the feelings are all on one side.'

As I'm in love with you. The words blazed through her mind like a burning streak of lightning, unexpected and without preamble. She swallowed hard, shaking her head as if to deny the knowledge that was too terrible to admit.

'You're not certain, then?' The hand on her throat had perceived the movement, and misunderstood its cause.

'I am.' She tried to stifle the sob that threatened to betray her. 'John hasn't changed.'

'Have you?'

Such a simple question. Yet it sounded the death knell to her confidence and assurance, to the expectations which till now she had taken for granted. As the long lean fingers continued their stroking with a persistence that made her quite dizzy, she wanted to say, 'Yes, I have changed, and all because you came into my life.'

'Well?' he asked again. 'Have you?'

There was only one answer. For John's sake, for all that had existed between them for as long as they both could remember, there could be only one answer. 'No,' she said low-toned, 'I haven't changed.' She hesitated. 'I never will.'

The fingers hardened, and he laughed shortly in the darkness, the sound harsh and derisive. 'Never is a long time. You'll learn that when you grow up.'

'I am grown up,' she threw at him.

'And you think you know all the answers. Tell me, spitfire, what will you do at Crocodile View? After the honeymoon you'll often be alone.'

'I'll find lots to interest me.' She was on her guard.

'You love animals?'

'Yes. They were always John's greatest interest, so I made them mine.' Dimly she was aware that she had given the wrong answer.

'I asked if *you* love animals.' There was a strange quality in his tone, as if something she had said had given him satisfaction.

'Of course.' Siane's voice was brittle with tension. 'In any case, it doesn't matter—whichever way you want to look at it.'

'I think it does.' Still that hateful hardness. 'You're chasing an illusion, spitfire. I don't give your marriage a chance.'

'I don't want to hear any more!' she shouted as she tried to pull away from him.

'Why not? Frightened you'll wake from your childish dreams?' He paused deliberately. 'You won't remain faithful to John for more than a month after your marriage.'

'How dare you!' Beside herself with fury, she lifted a hand to strike his cheek. He was too quick for her. She heard his swift intake of breath as he caught the hand and twisted it behind her.

'I'll show you how I dare,' he rasped.

His arms went around her, two bands of steel holding her closer than ever before, moulding her to him so that it seemed that two people became one. When one hand went to her blouse, tearing it from her skirt, she did not take the chance to pull away. The feel of hard fingers on her bare back, pushing around to find the fullness of a soft breast, was an agonising joy which transcended any desire to make an escape. His lips found hers, crushing them with a passion that was merciless, demanding and possessive. Beneath them her own lips parted, and the blood in her veins seemed to ignite with a fierce and fiery joy.

She did not struggle when he laid her down on the warm grass and lowered his weight on to hers. There was no coherent thought now, only the world of the senses, a wild clamouring to be possessed by him as a woman is possessed by the man she loves. She put her arms around his back and lay defence-less beneath him.

When he lifted himself from her, she could only look at him, bereft and hurt. The light of the stars showed a face that was hard and bleak, all angular lines and rugged contours. His lips were tight, but his eyes glittered with a wildness she had never seen there before.

'André. . . .' she whispered painfully.

'Well?' His voice was hard, like his expression.

Bewildered, she looked at him. For the moment there was no memory of the words that had passed between them. There was only an aching desire for his lovemaking.

'Do you want further proof?' The mockery in his tone pierced her with understanding. He had angered her often, but now she was angrier than she had ever been before. He had reduced her to a state of abandoned desire such as she had never experienced in her life, and all to prove a point.

With a strength she did not know she possessed she pushed away from him. He made no move to stop her as she ran towards the house. That would have been beneath him, she reflected bitterly. A morsel of humanity at a time when she felt belittled and humiliated, just a few words to say that he understood, these would have assuaged the hurt somewhat. But nothing would be forthcoming. Not from André Connors! In his supreme arrogance he was certain that he did understand. And therefore no comment or comfort would be necessary.

She snapped on the light in her room. The mirror showed her an image of herself she had not seen before. Her blouse was buttoned now, but untidily and askew, for she had pressed buttons into button-holes with trembling fingers as she ran. Her hair was dishevelled and her cheeks were flushed. In her eyes was wildness and confusion, mingled with despair. Would André understand if he could see her now? If so, it was just as well that he had not followed her. It was bad enough that he should think her abandoned and wanton. For him to know the truth would be totally unacceptable.

And what was that truth? she wondered, when she lay at last in her bed, staring sightlessly into the star-filled sky beyond her window. 'You won't stay faithful more than a month,' his taunt had been, and his lovemaking had been an attempt to prove the theory. He could hardly have been unaware of the completeness of her surrender. For his part he would now be satisfied that he had revealed her as a girl who was prepared to give herself fully to any man.

Would he think any differently if he knew the reason for her abandoned behaviour? That she was in love with him as she had never been in love in her life. That in the short time she had known him he had insinuated himself into her heart and her mind and her senses, so that sleeping or awake she could think only of him. That there was a yearning to be close to him, to touch him, to hear him talk of the things that mattered to him.

If he knew the truth, would he re-assess his opinion? Perhaps.... And yet it was better that he did not know. In fact, she thought desperately, he must *never* know. For at this stage she could no longer go back on her promise to John. She was in love with André: she knew that now. A crazy irrational love that knew no reason, no logic. But she loved John too, in a different way. She had always loved him, always would. And it was with John that all her loyalties must lie.

She would marry John, this week perhaps. And she would live with him at Crocodile View and make him as happy as she knew how. There would be times when she would have to meet André socially, though she would try to avoid him as much as she could. It would not be easy. It would be hard to meet his gaze, loaded with mockery and contempt, and to look back without flinching. But if he knew that she loved him it would be doubly hard.

'Come for me, John,' she sent out her silent appeal. 'I don't know how much longer I can bear to be at Pinelands.'

CHAPTER NINE

Breakfast was a lonely meal, but Siane was glad. She had slept unusually late, and when she came into the dining-room the sun was already high in the sky. André, she learned from Maria, rose early and was already out in the timber plantation. He had left instructions that she was to have whatever she wanted, and that he would be back at the house before lunch. For a moment she was taken aback by his consideration. It seemed totally out of character. And then she understood that it was not out of character at all. André Connors was the master of this great estate, and he was doing no more than showing her the politeness any other guest would have received. In a way it was that very politeness which seemed to put her firmly in her place.

Barbara Sinclair arrived as she was finishing her breakfast. She looked immaculate in a scarlet pant-suit, and Siane was uncomfortably aware of her own much simpler attire.

'For a stowaway you've certainly made yourself comfortable.' There was a biting hardness in the woman's voice and eyes as she watched Siane mop up a blob of apricot jam with one of Maria's freshly-baked scones.

'I *am* comfortable, thank you,' Siane returned

with a smoothness foreign to her. The woman's perfection made her feel ill at ease.

Apparently it was not the answer Barbara expected. For a moment she looked nonplussed. Then anger, barely disguised, appeared in her face. 'When are you going to Crocodile View?'

'When John comes for me.'

'That could be days.'

'Perhaps,' Siane agreed, more equably than she felt.

'And in the meantime you don't care that you're compromising André.' There was such hostility in the icy eyes that Siane was repelled. The thought of André married to this creature was not to be borne. Arrogant and self-sufficient he might be, but the hours in the timber plantation and at the sawmill had revealed that he was also dedicated and hard-working and possessed of an integrity which she could not help but respect. Yesterday she had mentally wished André and Barbara joy of each other. But that had been in temper. Today she knew that the thought of Barbara as André's wife brought only unhappiness. And then, with a flash of honesty, she knew that any wife of André's would bring her unhappiness.

'I think André knows how to take care of himself,' Siane said quietly. 'If he feels compromised he certainly hasn't given any indication of it.'

'Because he's a gentleman.'

'And I'm not a lady?' Siane felt her dislike for Barbara increase by the second.

'Remember that *you* said it,' Barbara remarked nastily. She paused. 'For your own sake, as well as that of your future husband, I suggest you make other arrangements.'

'Meaning that you want me to leave Pinelands?'

'Precisely.' No attempt at superficial politeness.

Siane studied the face opposite her. It would have been even more beautiful but for the iciness in the eyes and the hostile lines around the mouth. At length, she observed, 'You're not all that sure of your position, are you?'

There was a whitening around the nostrils, and the hands with the perfectly painted red nails clenched. 'I'm quite sure, Miss O'Brien. But I don't care to have the good name of my future home besmirched by a shameless brat.'

'I'm neither shameless nor a brat,' Siane said, low-toned, battling to keep her temper. 'But you're selfish and smug and an ice-maiden. André doesn't deserve you.'

'Be careful what you say, Siane O'Brien,' came the furious hiss. 'I can make trouble for you with John. Isn't it enough that André despises you?'

Had they laughed about her together? Sick at heart, Siane looked down, concealing the angry tears that pricked treacherously at her eyelids. A little while ago she had thought she would be able, in her own fashion, to carry off any social encounters with André and his wife. Now she knew that she would avoid them altogether.

'I think I should tell you that once I'm married

to André,' Barbara was saying, 'Pinelands will be more discriminating as to the guests it receives.'

'That will be your privilege.' Siane lifted her head and looked at Barbara Sinclair, and something in her eyes must have made the other woman realise she should make her own departure before the pot of jam landed in her face. Siane kept her face composed and her body poised until Barbara's car had vanished from sight at the end of the drive. Only then did she realise that her hands were trembling.

She would not stay any longer at Pinelands, she decided. The question remained how she could get to Crocodile View. André had covered the distance in a little more than three-quarters of an hour. Siane did not know of a bus that went to the game park. Under normal circumstances she would even have considered walking. It would take a few hours, but John could come back for her luggage. Right now she was angry enough to feel that she could manage it.

But even through her fury she remembered the danger. The camp was in the centre of the game park, and wild game roamed the bush for miles around it.

That left only another stowaway. But that was impossible, even assuming someone was going that way. It was bad enough that she had stowed away once. People would forget the incident in time—if Barbara Sinclair allowed them to. But another stowaway would cause too much disapproval in a country district where people were all known to one another.

Siane's behaviour would be a liability to John; it could even affect his job. She could not allow that to happen.

There was nothing for it but to wait at Pinelands and try to be patient.

Patience was never more difficult. The house was quiet and André was nowhere to be seen. In the living-room was a bookcase with rows of well-worn novels, many of which Siane would have liked to read. But there was no point in beginning a book which she would not be able to finish. She took some magazines from a rack and stepped through the french doors of the dining-room on to the patio.

Now and then she lifted her eyes from the pages to gaze restlessly over the forests falling away into the valley. After the conversation with Barbara Sinclair, and the implication that André had told her all that had passed between Siane and himself, she felt that she never wanted to see him again. It was irrational that at the same time she should wonder where he was, and what he was doing.

Hearing a car approaching, she sat up and shaded her eyes. A jeep was pulling up in front of the house, a different vehicle this time from the one in which she had stowed away. André must have several vehicles. . . . And then the driver was getting out of the jeep, and he wasn't André at all. He was John.

Siane stared down at him for one incredulous moment. And then she dropped the magazine to the floor, jumped from her chair, and ran down the steps and along the drive to meet him.

'John! Oh, John, you're here!' As he put his arms out to her she gave a tiny leap, so that her feet left the ground as her own arms went about his neck.

He held her for a moment, then put her gently down on the ground.

'John!' she exclaimed again. 'Oh, I'm so glad you've come. How did you know?'

'Bush news travels fast.' He grinned ruefully. 'I haven't even had a chance to say hello to you, sweetheart.'

'Surprised that I'm here?' She looked up at him, thinking that he was not as tall as André, for she did not need to tilt back her head to see into his eyes.

'To put it mildly!' he chuckled. 'Why didn't you let me know you were coming?'

'I was scared that you'd say we still had to wait. And I knew that was nonsense.' The words bubbled from her. Dimly she knew that she had to keep talking, as if in an attempt to recapture some of her old enthusiasm. 'Besides, I wanted to surprise you.'

'You certainly succeeded in that!'

'And you're not angry?' She stared into the beloved and familiar face of the man she'd known since they both were children. She had never been wary with him, or on her guard. John was a part of her. There had never been any reason for the politenesses and appearances so often assumed when people didn't want each other to know their true thoughts or feelings. But she had detected a new note in his tone when he'd spoken, one she did not remember hearing before, and she was puzzled.

When he did not reply right away, she repeated the question, more hesitantly this time. 'John— you're not angry?'

'Have I ever been angry with you, Siane?'

Spitfire, André would have called her in similar circumstances. But this was John, and if for a moment she had thought she imagined an undertone she did not understand, at least the smile was the same, and the laughter lines around eyes that were blue and steady.

'No. It's just that ... well, I suppose I could have let you know.' Why was she apologising? Never before had there been any need for apologies in their relationship.

'John, I stowed away....'

'Without thinking of the consequences.' He did not approve, that much was clear, but there was no mockery or derision in his manner as there would have been in André's. He went on gently, 'Don't look so stricken, sweetheart. It wasn't the most sensible thing to do, but at least it turned out well.' He paused. 'I'm very grateful that the man was André Connors.'

'You are ...?' She was suddenly confused. If he knew what had happened between them, and how her feelings for André were the most intense she had ever experienced, he would not be grateful at all. But it was something she would never tell him.

John took her hand, and they made their way out of the heat and back to the shaded patio. It was comforting to feel her hand in his. It took her back to the time when they had run together through the long grass in search of birds and nests and the small wild things of the veld. But it was also disconcerting to realise, now that she knew that a touch could provoke a tingling that was electric, that comfort was all she felt.

'André is the most insufferable man I ever met,' she said defensively.

'Is that how you see him?' John was amused. 'I've heard other women use altogether different terms to describe him.'

Other women.... Odd how just the two words used in association with André could bring the little ache to her chest. She changed the subject. 'Are we going to Crocodile View now?'

'Yes.'

'I suppose we'll have to find André and ... and tell him.'

'He knows. I stopped at the saw-mill on my way to the homestead.'

Siane waited a moment before answering. What had André's reaction been to John's coming? Was there a message for her? When John did not speak she felt stupidly deflated. If she thought about it logically, she knew that André would have said nothing. But it was hard to hold on to logic when she was flooded with disappointment.

She dropped her eyes, 'I see.' And then, horrified at the tonelessness in her voice, she injected a note of brightness. 'I'll just run in and get my things.'

'No, Siane.'

'My luggage, John.' She was puzzled. 'My case, and the wedding-dress, and, guess what....' She smiled at him. 'I even brought you some cookies.'

'Bring the cookies,' he grinned. 'Leave the rest. Sweetheart, it will take me a few days to get all the arrangements finalised.'

'I know, but....'

'André agrees with me that it would be better if you remained at Pinelands until then.'

She stared at him, and there was nothing she could do about the trembling that assailed her.

John saw her distress. 'Just a few days,' he said gently, running a hand through her tumbled curls.

'But I want to come with you! I want to be with you for the rest of my life.'

She saw a slight shadow flit across his face. It was a momentary thing, so quick that she thought afterwards she must have imagined it. 'We've so much time, sweetheart. I'll come to see you every day.' He paused. 'You look so upset, Siane. It won't be more than a few days.'

'John....' There was a hint of despair in her tone. 'I don't understand. We've been together all our lives. We went camping once. Oh, you must remember!'

He looked at her steadily. 'Of course I remember. But we were children then. You're a woman now, sweetheart. And I'm a man.'

'If it was any other two people I'd understand. But with us, it's different....' Her voice trailed away. She could not tell him that there would be no wild clamouring inside her, no aching need to have him make love to her. There would be only the comfort of a long and loving friendship, the re-assurance of having that friendship cemented into the deeper security of marriage.

'There are also proprieties to consider.'

'And here at Pinelands, are there no dangers, no proprieties?' she questioned wildly. 'If you're a man, so is André.'

'There's only one bedroom in my rondawel. Pine-lands is big, and André assures me that Maria will be sleeping in the house.'

As if the presence of a chaperone could quell the yearning inside her! The time for that was long past. If indeed, she realised with a flash of self-knowledge, there had ever been such a time from the first moment that she had met André.

'Don't make it hard for me, Siane,' John was say-ing. She heard the firmness in his tone, and knew that there was nothing she could do.

They talked as they drove through the forests, but until they were out of the Pinelands estate Siane's mind was only partly on what they were saying. Much as she tried not to think of André, it was hard not to let her eyes stray to the little paths that ran through the forests, as she wondered all the time if she would see him.

'I had another visitor this morning,' she said when they had passed through the big wrought iron gates and were on the national road. 'Barbara Sinclair. Do you know her?'

'Everyone knows Barbara.' She heard the amusement in his tone.

'She doesn't like me being at Pinelands. She was really quite nasty.'

'Don't let her bug you, sweetheart.' He reached for her hand and stroked it reassuringly.

'She said....' Siane tried to quell her breathlessness, and though she did not quite succeed, she pressed on. 'John, she says that she and André are going to be married.'

'She's certainly chased him a long time,' John said musingly.

'Will she get him?' Siane stopped breathing as she waited for his reply.

'My guess is she will.'

'Does André love her?' Siane's voice was very low.

'We've never discussed the matter.' John grinned. 'Barbara Sinclair's not my kind of woman, but in many ways she'll be a suitable wife for André.'

Siane would have liked to probe further, to ask in what way Barbara would be a suitable wife. But for once she managed to curb her impulses and remain silent. She knew it all already. Barbara was beautiful and poised, she would make the perfect hostess, be a presentable escort at any business function André might attend. Did she love André? Siane wondered if the icy woman with the perfect features could love anyone but herself. Did André love her? Maybe. But the thought gave her such pain that it was only with a grim effort of will that she managed to push it to the back of her mind, as she and John began to talk of other things. There was much to discuss. They talked about the wedding, and the arrangements John would have to make. They talked about Crocodile View, and of John's job. There was much that she knew already, but letters could never reveal all that speech could convey, and Siane was attentive and interested. After a while they talked about the people they both knew, and they laughed together at private jokes and things that happened in the past.

Siane sat sideways, watching John as he drove. She felt a great surge of affection for him. With André she was taut and tense and excited; with John she was relaxed and at ease. Without volition André's words came back to taunt her: 'You don't marry a brother.' She shifted restlessly in her seat. She and John were not brother and sister. They were cherished and beloved companions. There were no secrets between them—except one, and that one she would never divulge. There would be no surprises. Theirs would be a completely happy marriage, gentle and peaceful and secure.

John wanted to know how she had come to stow away in André's truck When she told him how she had hidden beneath the canvas, with her wedding-dress for a pillow, he was amused. 'Impulsive and a little crazy,' he said when he had finished laughing. 'Still the same Siane.'

Not quite the same. But she could not say it. And was he still the same John? It came to her, with a

slight sense of shock, that he was not. Basically he
had not changed. And yet there were differences. He
was thinner, surer, his expression had a deepened
maturity. And mixed with the gentleness was a sadness which had not been there before.

'What is it?' she wanted to ask him. 'What's happened to you?' But strangely, incredibly almost, she
was suddenly shy. This was John, with whom she
had always been able to talk of anything that
entered her mind. Yet here was a question she could
not ask.

They came to Crocodile View, and then to the
camp. John drew up the jeep beneath the shade of
a spreading maroela tree, then took her into the
rondawel which she had first entered with André.

'Will you be happy here, Siane?'

'Of course,' she said steadily. 'It's what we've always wanted, isn't it?'

'Yes, sweetheart, it is.' There was an intense
gentleness in his tone, but in his eyes was the look
of sadness she had noticed before. Was something
wrong that she did not know about? If so she should
not be surprised, for she had gathered as much from
his letters, without his ever mentioning anything
specific. Once she would have asked him straight
out what it was. But this John was not quite the
John she had known. Or was it just that they must
learn to know each other again after the long separa-
tion?

She felt a small surge of despair. If the year apart
had caused a gap of some kind, the sooner it was

breached the better.

'John.' She looked up at him urgently. 'You haven't kissed me.'

He smiled down at her. 'There's hardly been an opportunity.'

'I know.' André had made the opportunity when it did not exist. 'But now ... we're alone. ... Please, John.'

He took her in his arms, and she felt his lips in her hair. 'You're very lovely, Siane. Very beautiful.' She put her head back and looked at him, and then his arms tightened and his lips came down on hers.

He had kissed her many times. As children there had been kisses on birthdays and at Christmas, spontaneous kisses of greeting or excitement. As they had grown into their late teens and their friendship had changed and blossomed into the beginnings of a man–woman relationship, so their kisses had become romantic, gentle still, but edged with passion. Siane had enjoyed John's lovemaking, and knew he had enjoyed it too. There had been brief romances with others in between; a boy Siane had met on holiday, a girl John knew from work. But always they came together again, best content in each other's company.

Now he was kissing her again. But this was a new kiss, one she had never experienced with him before. The gentleness was still there; John could never be anything but gentle. But there was a roughness too, and a kind of despair which caught at Siane's heart.

She put her arms around his neck, kissing him in

return as lovingly as she knew how, as if to drive the sadness from him. Gradually she would discover what had happened to her John while they had been apart, but whatever the problem it was deep-seated. She could not probe, it would have to emerge on its own. In the meanwhile she could only love him, and hope that the marriage would bring him contentment.

And what of herself? she wondered miserably, as she pressed her body close to his. She was kissing John because she loved him with a love that was born of affection and cherished companionship. But the last few days had taught her that a different kind of love existed also. A love in which the touch of lips and hands and bodies called forth a pounding answering of the senses, a love which could push Siane to heights of ecstasy she had never dreamed possible. The love of a woman for a man, basic and primitive and wonderful.

For a short time, painfully short, she had known that kind of love. No matter that it was not returned, nor that André had made love to her purely for motives of his own. She knew now that it existed. She knew too that when John made love to her after they were married, when they clung together in the darkness of the night, it would require a super-human control not to let herself think of André and the rapture which she had so briefly experienced.

She would have to be careful never to let John know her true feelings. He would be deeply hurt if she did, and he was the one person in all the world whom Siane never could hurt.

At length John lifted his head, and the eyes that looked into hers held the ghost of a smile. 'Shall we leave off now till I've made an honest woman of you?'

'If we must.' She answered his smile with one of her own. It hurt to pretend with John. She had never needed to pretend with him before. All she could hope for was that the madness in her blood would fade with time, so that her relationship with her husband would have the same depth of honesty it had possessed when they were only friends.

In a corner of the room was a kitchenette. Siane filled a kettle, then put out cups and saucers and a small plate of biscuits. While they waited for the water to boil they took up their conversation where they had left off to kiss. She had already brought John up to date with much of what had happened at home. Now it was his turn to talk. He told her about the reserve, of his problems with poachers, and of the drought which had left hundreds of animals thirsty and homeless. The old enthusiasm was in his eyes when he spoke of his work. At least in one way her John had not changed, Siane realised.

Bit by bit a picture emerged of the way they would live. There would be loneliness, but this was a factor she had reckoned with. There would also be companionship. And there would be ways in which she could help John in his work. As a child she had learned to interest herself in his passion for animals. As a grown woman she would rekindle that interest—dormant in the time that John had been away, for Siane's own interests were of a slightly different nature. The more she could find to fill her time, the less chance there would be to brood.

CHAPTER TEN

When they had finished their tea they left the camp in the jeep. John had been away in the bush for three days, and now there were things he needed to do. The day after tomorrow, he said, they would drive into the nearest town to make arrangements for their marriage. They would see a vicar and find out about a special licence. Then they would make a few essential purchases. As soon as he could take off more time, they would go shopping. They would stay in town a few days and Siane would be able to choose new furniture. Soon, he told her smiling, they would have a bigger house. He would start on the plans as quickly as he could. Had he known she was coming he would have had it built already.

'I guess I really should have let you know I was coming,' she observed ruefully.

'My old impulsive Siane.' He took her hand and squeezed it. 'Don't ever change.'

But I've changed already, she thought miserably, and so have you. And perhaps there's not much either of us can do about it.

Driving through the bush with John was very different from touring the Kruger Park with her parents. With John there was nothing hit-or-miss. For him everything had its relevance—a flattened bush, the smudge of a footmark, a wheeling vulture, the alertness of an impala and the direction in which it sniffed the wind. His tone was eager when he talked about the bushveld, and of the birds and animals which made it their home. Listening to him, watching him, Siane thought that in this respect at least John had not changed. He had known what he wanted from the time he was a young child. Now that he had it, he loved it still.

'How will you feel about nursing orphans?' he asked her.

'Orphans?'

'Occasionally I bring in a baby animal whose mother's been killed.'

'That's not leaving things to nature, is it?' Siane was puzzled.

'Perhaps not. But there are times when a tiny animal's chances of survival are very slight. I like to give it that chance.' He paused. 'Will you take over that side of things for me, Siane?'

John had always brought home stray puppies and kittens, and together they had looked after them. Puppies and kittens were one thing, nature's small wild orphans quite another. But she would learn to look after a baby impala. She had always learned to do the things John expected of her, Siane reflected.

She smiled at him. 'I think I'd like it. If you'll show me how.'

John made the day so interesting that there were times when Siane actually managed to forget her absorption with André. It was only when they were driving to Pinelands that the enormity of her emotions hit her once more.

She turned to John. 'Let me stay with you.'

'Not for another few days, Siane.'

'Please. . . .' She did not know that her voice throbbed with despair. 'I don't want to go back to Pinelands, to André. . . .'

Blue eyes regarded her steadily, questioningly, 'Why do you dislike André so much?'

'He . . . he's arrogant. And . . . so hard.'

John was quiet a moment. Then he said, 'He's really brushed you up the wrong way. Sweetheart, don't be too hard on André. If he's hard with women, there could be a reason.'

'A reason?' Her head jerked up.

'His mother left Pinelands when he was a little boy.'

'I . . . I didn't know that,' she said breathlessly. 'Why did she leave?'

'She couldn't take the life, the loneliness.' His eyes were thoughtful. 'It isn't an easy life for a woman.'

'What happened to André? Did she take him with her?' Somehow she knew the answer to that before John spoke. For it would make other things fall into place—André's contempt for women, his belief that the city girl from Johannesburg would not last in the game park. That she would not be faithful.

'She met a man. They went off together. André was brought up by his father.'

It was the answer Siane had expected. Urgently she said, 'And yet there *are* women who can take the life. There *must* be, John.'

'Yes,' he said steadily, 'there are.' He smiled. 'You're one of them. I don't imagine that André's mother had your kind of spirit, sweetheart.'

'Yes, well. . . .' Restlessly she shifted in her seat. 'All this has nothing to do with me staying at Pinelands. I don't want to.' Her voice throbbed with appeal. 'John, you don't know. . . . I mean. . . . André was so angry when he found me.'

'That's understandable.' John chuckled. 'Siane, we've discussed this. It won't be for long. The days will pass quickly.'

Not quickly enough to prevent me losing my heart altogether, making it so hard for me to get this man out of my blood that I might have him haunting me for the rest of my life.

But further protest would not be understood without explanation. And that was the one thing she could not do.

André was in the garden, oiling a small wooden fence. He invited John to stay for dinner, but John refused, saying there were things he had to do at the camp before nightfall. 'I'll see Siane tomorrow,' he said. And, turning to her, 'I'll pick you up after breakfast.'

'Another tour of the park?' André asked when the jeep was a cloud of dust at the end of the road.

'In a way.' She took a quick breath. 'And the day after tomorrow we'll drive to Nelspruit to make arrangements for the wedding.'

She did not know that her eyes were wide and blue and filled with emotion as she looked up at him. She saw only the rigidity in the long line of the jaw, the implacability in the grey eyes that studied her. There was no softness in the granite mask of his face, only a grim hardness, as if he disapproved of what he saw.

'So you're getting what you wanted.' She heard the mocking note that she hated.

'What we both have wanted all along.' It was not easy to counter with defiance, when she yearned to hide her face against his chest and let tears give vent to her grief.

'You really believe that, don't you?'

She could not help flinching at his tone. 'Of course. Why not?'

'If you weren't such a child you'd know without being told.'

Evidently the last few days had not altered André's opinion of her as a person: he still did not consider her good enough for John. Now she understood the reason. But it still did not give him the right to speak as he did.

'What about Barbara Sinclair?' she countered recklessly. 'You think only you know what's right for people. When you marry that woman you'll be tied to an ice-maiden.'

He looked so angry that for a moment she thought he would hit her. Then his mouth relaxed, and a gleam appeared in his eyes. 'Shall we leave Barbara out of this?' he suggested.

'You *are* going to marry her?' She was intruding too far, but something drove her on.

'My plans are my own,' he said smoothly. 'Unlike you. I do know what I want. Shall we go back to the house?'

She was achingly aware of him as she walked beside him. She did not look at him, she did not need to. Every inch of the tall lean body, muscled and bronzed, was vividly imprinted in her mind. He did not touch her, did not even talk to her, and yet, as always, the aura of compelling masculinity which was with him at all times seemed to reach out and envelop her, making her quite dizzy with excitement. Once, when the path narrowed, his arm touched hers. The shock of the unexpected touch sent the adrenalin pumping through her system, and for a moment her chest was so tight that it was difficult to breathe. She cast a quick secret look at the man by her side. His face was without expression. The tingling that for her had been devastating had left him unaffected.

The sun was setting, and the sky was painted with the spectacular colours of an African sunset. The tops of the trees in the valley below were gilded with a vivid sheen, and the distant mountains were bathed in a translucent radiance. The scene had a wild and unearthly beauty which Siane, the city girl, had only rarely seen. Despite her unhappiness it came to her that she would have another memory of a time when she had been more crazily in love than she had believed possible. Already she had locked in her mind the adventure of the stowaway, and the sensual excitement when André had dried her trembling body with his towel. Now there would be also the beauty of the tropical sunset, with the bronzed figure of the man she loved striding silently at her side.

That night, as she lay sleepless in the dark, she knew that she would have been safer at Crocodile View with John. True, here at Pinelands she had a room of her own, and Maria, the housekeeper, slept in the house. But a sleeping chaperone was of little value when Siane's thoughts were centred on the man just three doors away. If he were to come to her now and take her in his arms, she did not think that she would have the strength to resist him.

Siane spent the next day at Crocodile View. She accompanied John in his jeep, and watched him go about the myriad tasks of a game-ranger. He would fetch her tomorrow, he said, and they would drive into Nelspruit to arrange for the marriage licence.

They returned at sunset to Pinelands to find that André had arranged a braaivleis, an informal party where Siane, as John's prospective wife, would meet the people who lived in the neighbourhood. At the news Siane felt tension knotting inside her. She was not ready for an encounter with people who would no doubt have learned of her escapade from the malicious lips of Barbara Sinclair. Nor did she feel she could stand to see that woman be André's hostess. Much as she would have to accustom herself to the situation, her emotions were at present so fragile that there were some things she could not yet endure.

She glanced at John. She had caught him off guard perhaps, for his lips were tight, and his expression was as tense as her own. Meeting her gaze, he smiled, as if to reassure her. But the one moment had been enough to reveal that he liked the idea of the party as little as she did. And no wonder, Siane thought. Like herself, John would resent André's arrogance and presumption in arranging the evening without consulting them first.

In one corner of the garden were two brick barbecue stands and already they had been prepared with wood and coal. As it grew dark, the fires were lit, so that by the time people were hungry the flames would have died sufficiently to put on the meat.

As the first guests began to arrive Siane was glad that she had taken trouble with her appearance. Mainly farming folk, everybody was eager to meet the girl who had stowed away in André Connors' truck. Barbara had spread the news well, for there were none who had not heard the story. But if Barbara had reckoned on disapproval she had underrated her audience. For the most part they were amused and interested, and all were friendly.

Siane tried to keep her eyes away from Barbara, who had assumed the role of hostess with an affectation that was nauseating. Siane exchanged only a few words of greeting with her, and then went out of her way to avoid her. Barbara's manner was so cool, so hostile—except when André was near, when she became simperingly friendly—that Siane knew she would lose her temper if she did not remove herself from the other girl's presence.

Lindy was there too, and Siane was struck again by the girl's unaffected sweetness. Lindy smiled and was friendly, but in her eyes was a look of distress which saddened Siane, for she knew only too well how the other girl was feeling. She would have liked to tell Lindy that she too was suffering from unrequited love. But of course it was something she could not do. Not that the girl could even be expected to be sympathetic in the circumstances. It was only natural that Lindy should be resentful of her, even if she did not let her feelings show. But Siane hoped that in time, when Lindy had found someone else to love, they could still be friends.

There was Lindy's father, a quiet distinguished-looking man, with the same eyes and direct expression as his daughter. He talked for a while to Siane, telling her a little about his work as a vet. While he talked Siane felt that he was assessing her, but she did not mind. Perhaps he knew Lindy's feelings, and she could not help liking the frank openness of the man.

It was quite dark by the time the meat was ready. The tantalising aroma of the braai wafted from the fires, mingling with the perfumes of the garden. The night was warm, and the air rang with talk and laughter. Siane had not seen much of John, but now he brought her a plate laden with boerewors, a hot buttered mielie and salad.

'Did you mind that André arranged the braai without telling us first?' Siane asked.

'Not at all.' But the quick denial was belied by an odd note in his tone.

'He's the original autocrat, isn't he?' Unaccountably there was a need for small-talk. 'He consults nobody, but just does what he wants.'

'There's little André does without an extremely good reason,' John said thoughtfully.

Oh, André did have his reasons, Siane knew that. And they concerned punishment of herself. But she swallowed the impulse to say it. There was a time when she could have said anything to John, and have known that she would be understood, even if he did not share her opinion. But this was the new John, still the dear companion she had always loved, yet subtly different somehow. In a sense it was ironic that now when she was on the verge of becoming his wife, she should feel strangely hesitant with him for the first time in her life.

When everyone had eaten there was dancing. There was taped music and a small wooden dance floor had been set near the trees. André, Siane had grudgingly admitted to herself, organised a party as expertly as he did everything else.

She danced with John first, and was glad to find that she still followed him with as much ease as before. And so it should be, for it was John who had taught her to dance to records in the living-room of her home. Together they had gone to school dances, and later to university balls. And now they were on the threshold of marriage, and they still danced in a unison so perfect that he hardly needed to lead her; from years of practice she already knew what his next step would be.

Somehow the dance was symbolic of their whole future. They would have their joys and their sorrows, their ups and their downs, but by and large there would be harmony, an accord of mind and spirit. Impulsively she looked up at him and smiled, and caught the answering smile in the upward curve of his lips.

'We *will* be happy.' She made the remark without thinking that he might think the emphasis strange. It was more an expression of her thoughts. It might never be possible to forget André, but the craziness which stirred in her now would be gradually stilled. And she and John really would be happy.

Her heart jerked when she saw the tall lean figure beside them. And then she realised that he was dancing with Barbara. She had both arms wound around his neck, and was laughing into his eyes, her lips close to his in what looked like an invitation. Siane stifled a sob as she turned her head and buried it against John's chest. She would not see them kiss —that was too much to expect of her.

The music ended and Siane was claimed by a tall man with laughing eyes, whose name she would not later remember. And after him there were others.

Everyone wanted to have a dance with her, intrigued perhaps by the newcomer to their community. Only André did not ask her to dance. She saw that he danced with most of the women, duty dances presumably, but for most of the time he was with Barbara.

When he did approach her she had almost given up hope. For a moment she considered refusing him, then she knew that she would only make herself even more childish in his eyes. She went into his arms with an expression of deliberate unconcern, and hoped he did not see that her lips were trembling.

She tried to make herself stiff and unresponsive, but the moment she felt the length of his body against hers her treacherous limbs were like water. André held her close, closer than was necessary, but there was no will left in her to fight him. No desire either. The music was slow, and the movements of his thighs against hers were achingly sensual. His fingers were cool and strong, and she could feel the rhythmic beat of his heart.

It was late and many of the guests, mostly farming folk and early risers, had already left. It had grown darker too, for clouds had gathered in the sky, dimming the radiance of the starlight. It was no longer possible to distinguish the faces of the people around her. To Siane it was as if they danced together on an island of isolation, just she and André quite alone. She did not think of the next day, when she and John would drive to town to arrange for their wedding. There was no room for thought. There was just the magic of André's arms around her, the scent of virile maleness, the joy of feeling him close.

The magic was shattered abruptly by Barbara's brittle call. 'André darling, our guests are leaving.'

Our.... A world of meaning in that one word. Siane was trembling when André left her, and she was glad of the darkness because nobody could see her tears. She thought she saw someone approaching, but she was in no mood to dance. Quickly she side-stepped and made for the dark haven of the trees.

She leaned against the trunk of a pine, glad of support for her shaking limbs. It was very dark here. At last she could let her tears fall.

It came to her only gradually that she was not alone. From somewhere very near her came the sound of voices. A pair of lovers who thought themselves private, she guessed, and decided to move elsewhere and leave them to their privacy. She was turning away when she recognised John's voice.

She stood quite still as her breath caught in her throat. Lindy's voice came to her then, very soft and indistinct. And yet it was Lindy. It came to Siane in a flash that it could not be anyone else.

Hardly breathing, not stopping to question her integrity in what she was doing, Siane tiptoed close. Through the darkness she could see two figures close together, the man with his arm about the girl.

'I'm so sorry, love,' John was saying, and his voice was low and filled with sorrow.

'I know....' Lindy gulped. Siane guessed that he was crying.

'It's all my fault. I should have written to her, and told her....' He was silent a few moments. 'Lindy darling, I can't let Siane down now. She's been so much to me all my life. This crazy thing she did ... that's Siane, eager and impulsive.'

'It's going to be hard.' Lindy was making a brave attempt to control herself, but there was a quiver in her tone.

'Sheer hell. Seeing you around, knowing how we feel....' He groaned. 'I've always loved Siane, and she loves me. But I don't love her in the way I love you. If only I'd written the truth! But I didn't. Lindy darling, I'm sorry.'

'And so you should be!' Impulsive to the last, Siane stepped through the trees.

Lindy gasped and drew away from John. John was silent and rigid.

'You—heard?' he asked after a moment, painfully.

'Every word. And thank goodness for that!' Siane spoke with a heartiness she did not feel. 'You *should* have written, John. I'd have understood.'

'Would you, Siane?'

'I ... I hope so.... I'd have been hurt, perhaps, but I'd have got over it.'

The long journey had been all for nothing. She could have been spared the agony of falling in love with a man who was so far above all other men that she did not know whether she would ever love again.

'Siane,' Lindy spoke for the first time, 'I'm sorry.'

'Don't be. You'll be good for John.' She heard the double intake of breath. She laughed softly and hoped they did not hear the tiny sob in her voice. 'Of course you must marry him. It's not every girl I'd hand him to. Because I really do love him.' She paused. 'But only as a brother.'

'Siane ... Siane, you mean that?' There was the throb of urgency in John's voice.

'Yes. Marry Lindy. You ... you're so right together.'

'What about you?'

It was more difficult to speak now. 'I ... I've known for two days that ... that I don't love you the way a wife should.'

'But you never told me.' John was puzzled. And then, 'You were doing the same as I was. You didn't want to let me down.' He was silent a moment, as if there was something he didn't understand. 'Why did you come? You must have thought....' He paused. When he spoke again she heard the understanding in his voice. 'There's someone else now?'

Siane was silent, the lump in her throat making it hard to swallow.

Lindy's voice rang through the dark. 'André! It *is* André, isn't it?'

'Yes,' Siane said dully. 'But he doesn't want me.'

'You're wrong!' Lindy sounded vibrant and positive. 'That afternoon in the stable-yard, I saw his face when he looked at you. And then you mentioned John and ... I'm afraid I was so shattered that I never gave it another thought.'

'André is going to marry Barbara,' Siane said with finality. 'I'm cold. I think I'll go up to the house.' She took a step towards the other girl and hugged her briefly. 'Look after my John for me, Lindy.'

She kissed John then. But she did not speak. The scene had affected her more than she had allowed her bravado to reveal. Besides, now as in the past, there was no need for words. John would understand.

She left the trees and skirted the lawn towards the house. The party was still in progress, but she had lost her zest for it. Now she wanted only to reach the sanctuary of her room and to do her packing. In the morning she would ask André if he would drive her to the nearest village from which she could take a bus back to the station at Wilgespruit. No matter if there was no bus for a few days. The village would have a hotel where she could wait.

However unappealing the prospect of that was, it was better than the thought of remaining any longer at Pinelands. Now that her engagement to John was broken, there was no longer a reason to stay even another day in André's house. If she could leave here tonight that would be even better. She knew that if ever she were to make anything of her life—and it would be a life which must now be completely restructured—her chances of success would be slight if she were to be forever haunted by André.

Nobody saw her as she made her way to the house, and Siane was glad. Explanations were the last thing she was ready for. In releasing John she had done the only thing possible, not only for his sake but also for her own. She had known before tonight that their marriage would be a mistake. But John was not an object of infatuation whom she had only known only a short time. Even if she did not love him in a romantic sense, her feelings for him were nevertheless very deep. The scene she had just been through had left her far more shaken than either John or Lindy would ever know.

It did not take her long to empty the wardrobe and put her clothes into her case. All that was left now was the dress which she wore. Quickly she drew it over her head, then slipped into a nightgown. She caught a glimpse of herself in the mirror. Shell-pink satin trimmed with delicate lace, the nightgown was one she had bought especially for her trousseau. Little had she thought then that she would be wearing it as she packed to return home alone.

She was folding the party dress into the case when she heard the door open. Instinctively her head jerked around, and the breath left her lungs at sight of the tall figure in the doorway, his broad shoulders blocking her only line of escape. He looked very tall, a sinuous Lucifer in a velour navy sweater belted into well-cut navy trousers. The dark eyes were lit by a gleam which sent the adrenalin pumping madly through Siane's nerve-stream. Would this be her last memory of the man? Not as she would see him tomorrow, in daylight, but the picture before her now. This image of wildness, of strength and power and danger. Devastatingly handsome and compellingly male. This was how she would remember him—a man beyond all other men. Had she been so foolish as to think she could escape being haunted by him for the rest of her life?

For a moment that had no meaning in time, she could only stare at him speechlessly. He did not make things easier for her in that he was quite silent. After the first stunned moment of shock it came to her that she was in her nightgown, the fragility of which left little to the imagination. With a quick movement she dropped the dress and covered her breasts with her hands.

His chuckle was low and sensuous. 'I've seen you in less, spitfire.'

So he *had* watched her climbing out of the pool. Numbly she shook her head, as if by so doing she could drive the memory of that morning from her mind.

'No point in denying it.' The laughter was still in his voice. His hands went to hers, taking them easily from their protective attitude against her chest. She could only stand helplessly, while his hands held hers low at her sides, and his eyes studied her, missing nothing of the figure as clearly outlined beneath the satin and lace as if Siane wore nothing at all.

'Nice,' he said softly, appreciatively. 'Very nice.' Another quality had been added to his tone, and Siane felt her heartbeat quicken. 'John doesn't know what he's giving up.'

'You know?' The startled whisper was torn from her throat.

'I know.' A hand went out to cup her chin, drawing her face upwards so that he could look into her eyes. 'You're upset, Siane?'

She did not answer at once, caught by the unexpected intensity of his gaze. Besides, it was becoming more and more difficult to breathe.

'You found John and Lindy together in the trees. Was that why you let him go?' He paused, staring down at her with a gaze that burned. 'Was it hurt pride?'

She shook her head, unable to speak.

Something flickered in the dark eyes, and she heard the swift intake of his breath. 'John says you'd both realised that your love wasn't that of a man and a woman. Is that true, Siane?'

At that moment it did not matter that André was soon to be married to Barbara, nor that she would be leaving with more pride if she took the trouble to invent an excuse. The hand was still on her chin, and the dark eyes were gazing into hers, seeking, probing, drawing out a truth which she was powerless to hide.

'Yes,' she said very softly, 'it's true.'

There was a look of satisfaction in his face which brought tears to her lashes. She tried to look away, but the hand was still firm under her chin. And then she realised that it no longer mattered if he read her emotions. Let him think her silly or shameless, there was no more pride left in her, no will to dissemble.

'And now,' he asked, 'what were you doing when I disturbed you?'

'Packing. I'm leaving here, André.'

'You are not,' he said firmly.

'What ... what do you mean?' Her eyes were wide and shimmering, and hope was springing wildly inside her. 'Now that my marriage is off ... I can't stay here.'

'As my wife you can, my darling spitfire.'

'Wife?' She could hardly articulate the word through the joy surging through her.

'Of course.' His voice was unexpectedly husky. 'Will you marry me?'

'But ... but Barbara ... she said....' Even now it was difficult to take in.

'Barbara's wishes have never coincided with my own.' André was smiling, but she could sense the impatience in the hands that were drawing her closer.

'Do you mean ...?' It was foolishly difficult to ask the question, even now.

'I love you, my darling impulsive little spitfire. I've loved you since the moment I found you lying on your wedding-dress in the back of my truck. Does that answer your question?'

'Oh, yes,' she whispered brokenly. 'And I love you. That's why....'

That's why I couldn't marry John, she wanted to

say, but his mouth closed on hers with a kiss that permitted no words. And after a moment she knew that no words were needed. André understood her now and for ever.

Take these best-selling
4 novels
FREE

That's right! FOUR first-rate Harlequin romance novels by four world renowned authors, FREE, as your introduction to the Harlequin Presents Subscription Plan. Be swept along by these FOUR exciting, poignant and sophisticated novels . . . . Travel to the Mediterranean island of Cyprus in **Anne Hampson**'s "Gates of Steel" . . . to Portugal for **Anne Mather**'s "Sweet Revenge" . . . to France and **Violet Winspear**'s "Devil in a Silver Room" . . . and the sprawling state of Texas for **Janet Dailey**'s "No Quarter Asked."

Harlequin Presents...

The very finest in romantic fiction

Join the millions of avid Harlequin readers all over the world who delight in the magic of a really exciting novel. SIX great NEW titles published EACH MONTH! Each month you will get to know exciting, interesting, true-to-life people . . . . You'll be swept to distant lands you've dreamed of visiting . . . . Intrigue, adventure, romance, and the destiny of many lives will thrill you through each Harlequin Presents novel.

Get all the latest books before they're sold out!

As a Harlequin subscriber you actually receive your personal copies of the latest Presents novels immediately after they come off the press, so you're sure of getting all 6 each month.

Cancel your subscription whenever you wish!

You don't have to buy any minimum number of books. Whenever you decide to stop your subscription just let us know and we'll cancel all further shipments.

What readers say about Harlequin Presents

"Harlequins take away the world's troubles and for a while you can live in a world of your own where love reigns supreme."
L.S.,* Beltsville, Maryland

"Thank you for bringing romance back to me."
J.W., Tehachapi, California

"I find Harlequins are the only stories on the market that give me a satisfying romance with sufficient depth without being maudlin."
C.S., Bangor, Maine

"Harlequins are magic carpets...away from pain and depression...away to other people and other countries one might never know otherwise."
H.R., Akron, Ohio

*Names available on request

Put more love into your life. Experience the wonderful world of...

Harlequin Romances

Six brand-new romantic novels every month, each one a thrilling adventure into romance...an exciting glimpse of exotic lands.

Written by world-famous authors, these novels put at your fingertips a fascinating journey into the magic of love, the glamour of faraway places.

Don't wait any longer. Buy them now.